GLIMMER TRAIN
STORIES

EDITORS
Susan Burmeister-Brown   Linda B. Swanson-Davies

CONSULTING EDITOR
Roz Wais

COPY EDITOR
Scott Stuart Allie

TYPESETTING & LAYOUT
Paul Morris

ADMINISTRATIVE ASSISTANT
Kaylin Elaine Dodge

COVER ARTIST
Jane Zwinger

PUBLISHED QUARTERLY
in spring, summer, fall, and winter by Glimmer Train Press, Inc.
1211 NW Glisan Street, Suite 207, Portland, Oregon 97209-3054
Telephone: 503/221-0836   Facsimile: 503/221-0837
www.glimmertrain.com
PRINTED IN U.S.A.
Indexed in *The American Humanities Index.*

Glimmer Train (ISSN #1055-7520), registered in U.S. Patent and Trademark Office, is published quarterly, $34 per
year in the U.S., by Glimmer Train Press, Inc., Suite 207, 1211 NW Glisan, Portland, OR 97209. Periodicals postage
paid at Portland, OR, and additional mailing offices. POSTMASTER: Send address changes to Glimmer Train Press,
Inc., Suite 207, 1211 NW Glisan, Portland, OR 97209.

ISSN # 1055-7520, **ISBN # 1-59553-000-2**, CPDA BIPAD # 79021

DISTRIBUTION: Bookstores can purchase *Glimmer Train Stories* through these distributors:
DEMCO, Inc., 4810 Forest Run Road, Madison, WI 53707 ph: 800/356-1200
Ingram Periodicals, 1226 Heil Quaker Blvd., LaVergne, TN 37086
Peribo PTY Ltd., 58 Beaumont Rd., Mt. Kuring-Gai, NSW 2080, AUSTRALIA
Source Interlink, 27500 Riverview Center Blvd., Suite 400, Bonita Sprints, FL 36134
Ubiquity, 607 Degraw St., Brooklyn, NY 11217
SUBSCRIPTION SVCS: EBSCO, Divine, Blackwell's UK

Subscription rates: Order online (www.glimmertrain.com)
or by mail—one year, $36 within the U.S. (Visa/MC/check).
Airmail to Canada, $46; outside North America, $59.
Payable by Visa/MC or check for U.S. dollars drawn on a U.S. bank.

*Attention established and emerging short-story writers: We pay $500 for first
publication and onetime anthology rights. We welcome your work via our online
submission procedure: www.glimmertrainpress.com*

Glimmer Train Press also offers **Writers Ask**—*nuts, bolts, and informed perspectives—
a quarterly newsletter for the committed writer. One year, four issues, $20 within the U.S.
($26 beyond the U.S.), Visa, MC, or check to Glimmer Train Press, Inc., or order online
at www.glimmertrain.com.*

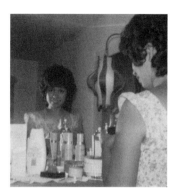

We'd like to dedicate this issue to Carmel, the wonderful woman
who fell in love with our father back in 1978.
(Our mother died in 1970, leaving him utterly bereft.)

Carmel has taught us so many things, helped us throw preconceptions
out our windows by the bucketload. (She is, mind you, twenty-eight
years younger than he is, and they married on their eighth date!) She
knows how to find pleasure and sweetness and something funny in all
corners. She embraces every person our father (and even our mother) has
ever loved. She welcomes us into their home, always, no matter what.
Our dad is nearly eighty-seven, but in spite of a litany of life-threatening
ailments, goes on with no fortification other than his love of family, of
life itself, and a deep love of his dear Carmel. For some reason, his
dementia seems to lift during the night, so when he awakes at 2 A.M.,
and says, *Are you awake?* She says, *Sure! Shall we have a bite to eat?* They
talk and they laugh; she encourages him to sing and look at the photos of
family gone on and family still here, but forgotten in the daylight hours.
He says his mother appeared to him! she reports joyously. *He was so pleased!*

And when we visit, though he may forget all of our names,
he says in warm greeting, *I love you, Dear. I have such a good life.*

Thank you, Carmel; thank you.

Susan & Linda

PAST CONTRIBUTING AUTHORS AND ARTISTS
Many of issues 1 through 50 are available for eleven dollars each.

Robert A. Abel • David Abrams • Linsey Abrams • Steve Adams • Diane King Akers • Susan Alenick • Rosemary Altea • Julia Alvarez • Brian Ames • A. Manette Ansay • Margaret Atwood • Kevin Bacon • Michael Bahler • Doreen Baingana • Aida Baker • Russell Banks • Brad Barkley • Andrea Barrett • Kyle Ann Bates • Richard Bausch • Robert Bausch • Charles Baxter • Ann Beattie • Barbara Bechtold • Cathie Beck • Jeff Becker • Janet Belding • Sallie Bingham • Kristen Birchett • Melanie Bishop • James Carlos Blake • Corinne Demas Bliss • Valerie Block • Joan Bohorfoush • Robin Bradford • Harold Brodkey • Danit Brown • Kurt McGinnis Brown • Paul Brownfield • Ayşe Papatya Bucak • Judy Budnitz • Susanna Bullock • Christopher Bundy • Jenny A. Burkholder • Evan Burton • Michael Byers • Christine Byl • Gerard Byrne • Jack Cady • Annie Callan • Kevin Canty • Peter Carey • Ioanna Carlsen • Ron Carlson • H. G. Carroll • David Cates • Brian Champeau • Vikram Chandra • Diane Chang • Mike Chasar • Xiaofei Chen • Robert Chibka • Chieh Chieng • Carolyn Chute • George Makana Clark • Dennis Clemmens • Aaron Cohen • Robert Cohen • Evan S. Connell • Ellen Cooney • Rand Richards Cooper • Lydia E. Copeland • Rita D. Costello • Wendy Counsil • Doug Crandell • Ronald F. Currie Jr. • William J. Cyr • Quinn Dalton • Bilal Dardai • Tristan Davies • C.V. Davis • Laurence de Looze • Toi Derricotte • Janet Desaulniers • Tiziana di Marina • Junot Díaz • Stephen Dixon • Matthew Doherty • Michael Dorris • Siobhan Dowd • Greg Downs • Eugenie Doyle • Tiffany Drever • Andre Dubus • Andre Dubus III • Stuart Dybek • Wayne Dyer • Melodie S. Edwards • Ron Egatz • Barbara Eiswerth • Mary Relindes Ellis • Susan Engberg • Lin Enger • James English • Tony Eprile • Louise Erdrich • Zoë Evamy • Nomi Eve • George Fahey • Edward Falco • Anthony Farrington • Merrill Feitell • J.M. Ferguson Jr. • Lisa Fetchko • Susan Fox • Michael Frank • Pete Fromm • Daniel Gabriel • Avital Gad-Cykman • Ernest Gaines • Tess Gallagher • Louis Gallo • Elizabeth Gallu • Kent Gardien • Ellen Gilchrist • Mary Gordon • Peter Gordon • Elizabeth Graver • Lisa Graley • Jo-Ann Graziano • Andrew Sean Greer • Gail Greiner • John Griesemer • Zoë Griffith-Jones • Paul Griner • Aaron Gwyn • L.B. Haas • Patricia Hampl • Christian Hansen • Elizabeth Logan Harris • Marina Harris • Erin Hart • Kent Haruf • Daniel Hayes • David Haynes • Daniel Hecht • Ursula Hegi • Amy Hempel • Andee Hochman • Alice Hoffman • Jack Holland • Noy Holland • Lucy Honig • Ann Hood • Linda Hornbuckle • David Huddle • Siri Hustvedt • Quang Huynh • Stewart David Ikeda • Lawson Fusao Inada • Elizabeth Inness-Brown • Debra Innocenti • Bruce Jacobson • Andrea Jeyaveeran • Charles Johnson • Leslie Johnson • Wayne Johnson • Allen Morris Jones • Thom Jones • Cyril Jones-Kellet • Elizabeth Judd • Tom Miller Juvik • Jiri Kajanë • Anita Shah Kapadia • Hester Kaplan • Wayne Karlin • Andrew Kass • Tom Kealey • Andrea King Kelly • Thomas E. Kennedy • Tim Keppel • Jamaica Kincaid • Lily King • Maina wa Kinyatti • Carolyn Kizer • Carrie Knowles • Clark E. Knowles • N.S. Köenings • Jonathan Kooker • David Koon • Karen Kovacik • Jake Kreilkamp • Marilyn Krysl • Frances Kuffel • Mandy Dawn Kuntz • Anatoly Kurchatkin • Victoria Lancelotta • Frances Lefkowitz • Jennifer Levasseur • Doug Lawson • Don Lee • Peter Lefcourt • Jon Leon • Doris Lessing • Debra Levy • Janice Levy • Christine Liotta • Rosina Lippi-Green • David Long • Nathan Long • Salvatore Diego Lopez • Melissa Lowver • William Luvaas • Barry Lyga • David H. Lynn • Richard Lyons • Bruce Machart • Jeff MacNelly • R. Kevin Maler • George Manner • Jana Martin • Lee Martin • Valerie Martin • Alice Mattison • Jane McCafferty • Judith McClain • Cammie McGovern • Cate McGowan • Eileen McGuire • Susan McInnis • Gregory McNamee • Jenny Drake McPhee • Amalia Melis • Frank Michel • Nancy Middleton • Alyce Miller • Katherine Min • Mary McGarry Morris • Ted Morrissey • Mary Morrissy • Bernard Mulligan • Abdelrahman Munif • Manuel Muñoz • Karen Munro • Kent Nelson • Thisbe Nissen • Sigrid Nunez • N. Nye • Ron Nyren • Joyce Carol Oates • Tim O'Brien • Vana O'Brien • Mary O'Dell • Chris Offutt • Jennifer Oh • Laura Oliver • Felicia Olivera • Thomas O'Malley • Stewart O'Nan • Elizabeth Oness • Karen Outen • Mary Overton • Patricia Page • Ann Pancake • Peter Parsons • Roy Parvin • Karenmary Penn • Susan Perabo • Dawn Karima Pettigrew • Constance Pierce • Steven Polansky • John Prendergast • Jessica Printz • Melissa Pritchard • E. Annie Proulx • Eric Puchner • Kevin Rabalais • Jonathan Raban • George Rabasa • Margo Rabb • Mark Rader • Paul Rawlins • Nancy Reisman • Linda Reynolds • Kurt Rheinheimer • Anne Rice • Michelle Richmond • Alberto Ríos • Roxana Robinson • Paulette Roeske • Stan Rogal • Carol Roh-Spaulding • Frank Ronan • Elizabeth Rosen • Janice Rosenberg • Jane Rosenzweig • Karen Sagstetter • Kiran Kaur Saini • Mark Salzman • Carl Schaffer • Libby Schmais • Natalie Schoen • Adam Schuitema • Jim Schumock • Lynn Sharon Schwartz • Barbara Scot • Amy Selwyn • Catherine Seto • Bob Shacochis • Evelyn Sharenov • Sally Shivnan • Daryl Siegel • Ami Silber • Al Sim • George Singleton • Floyd Skloot • Brian Slattery • Roland Sodowsky • Scott Southwick • R. Clifton Spargo • Gregory Spatz • Brent Spencer • L.M. Spencer • Lara Stapleton • Barbara Stevens • John Stinson • George Stolz • William Styron • Virgil Suárez • Karen Swenson • Liz Szabla • Mika Tanner • Lois Taylor • Paul Theroux • Abigail Thomas • Randolph Thomas • Joyce Thompson • Patrick Tierney • Aaron Tillman • Tamara B. Titus • Andrew Toos • Pauls Toutonghi • Vu Tran • Patricia Traxler • Jessica Treadway • Doug Trevor • William Trevor • Rob Trucks • Kathryn Trueblood • Carol Turner • Christine Turner • Kathleen Tyau • Michael Upchurch • Lee Upton • Gerard Varni • Katherine Vaz • A. J. Verdelle • Daniel Villasenor • Sergio Gabriel Waisman • Daniel Wallace • Ren Wanding • Mary Yukari Waters • Jonathan Wei • Jamie Weisman • Lance Weller • Ed Weyhing • J. Patrice Whetsell • Joan Wickersham • Lex Williford • Gary Wilson • Robin Winick • Terry Wolverton • Monica Wood • Christopher Woods • Leslie A. Wooten • wormser • Celia Wren • Callie Wright • Calvin Wright • Brennen Wysong • June Unjoo Yang • Nancy Zafris • Jane Zwinger

CONTENTS

*I've always liked this photo because it reminds me of what
we look like when we're still too young to have a past.*

Robert Schirmer's short-story collection *Living with Strangers* won the Bobst Award
for Emerging Writers and was published by NYU Press. He's been the recipient of
an O. Henry Award and a Pushcart Prize, as well as fellowships from the Chesterfield
Film Company's Writer's Film Project and the Sewanee Writers' Conference. Recently
he completed a novel and a second collection of stories.

TRAIN WRECK WITH CATTLE

Robert Schirmer (signature)

Robert Schirmer

What drove me to the railroad bridge that afternoon, and what I planned to do once I got there, no longer matters. I wasn't myself then, or else I was too wholly myself, confused and off balance, so dreamy I wouldn't have recognized myself passing on a well-lighted road. The lack of medication partially condemned me. I'd run out of Prozac, that great equalizer, and wasn't in the mood to drive into town for the refill. Only a masochist would stomach the doctor's unspoken admonishments, the solemn looks of pity through his hot liquid eyes, as if chemicals had leaked into his tears. Besides, Julie needed the car to drive to work, and it was a mile and a half into town.

After Julie had gone I took my place on a lawn chair in the weedy backyard, deceiving myself into thinking I might be okay for a stretch without medication. I had not worked a job in over three months. I knew I should work, had to work, a good man worked when necessary, and work was work. But this was Scranton, Minnesota: on a map it could be lost under a crumb of devil's food cake. The work available in that depressed elbow of a town would have buried me, and like most men I'd rather be dead than buried, so I held off from day to day, hoping that something promising might be waiting just ahead.

To help relax me I'd brought out to the yard a copy of *Moby Dick*. I had every intention of improving myself with my free time, only the book seemed to fade away as soon as I looked down into it. The words spilled off the page onto my lap—scattered, unreadable words, expecting me to make sense of them (a dark drizzly November in my damp soul, that didn't sound right). I'd dog-eared several pages of the book when I was enrolled in a college far from Scranton, studying psychology and 19th-century American lit before I dropped out to pursue a life of hunger, dead-end jobs, and short change. Some of the pages carried marginal notes I must have pencilled in a decade ago. I could read my own annotations well enough, and they suggested I knew what I was doing back then, or else I'd faked it with conviction. It was unsettling to encounter my past scrawl, though, a little like hearing the Iago of a younger self whispering into my ear and poisoning me against who I'd become. I looked up from the book, wiped my eyes, and stared through a knothole in the fence that divided our yard from a stretch of grassy field. Ground, sky, only there seemed little clear division between where one ended and the other began. The sky looked as if it had crashed into the earth, or else the grass had taken root inside the clouds. Don't listen to whoever insists he doesn't know how the hell the two could be mistaken. He's the guy who will look at a zebra and see black and white instead of gray, or who believes in divine order when we all have our lives to prove divine chaos.

Julie came home for lunch and found me in this state, contemplating creation with *Moby Dick* open like a split stone across my lap. She was angry and I couldn't fault her for that. The bills … the ridiculous rent on this claptrap house, and we were falling behind … plus, I was a good-looking man, but had not shaven in three days. "You deserve better than me," I said as I trailed her into the house, counting on my self-reproach to blunt her bad mood.

She lay down on the bed in her short, tight secretary's number and threw an exhausted arm over her face. "An egg-salad sandwich waiting for me, maybe some decaf," she said. "That's all I wanted."

I lay beside her and kissed her mouth in abject apology. Abject, a pitiable word, but sometimes it applies. "You haven't showered," she complained. "And your breath isn't brushed."

Once I was a good lover, although this may be difficult for realists to believe now. I tried to love Julie out of her anger and disappointment. Only I couldn't seem to focus. No matter how tenderly I kissed her mouth, tongue, throat, I would lose sense of my own mouth, my own weighty tongue, and stop to touch it so I would remember its truth.

Then I fell asleep. Open mouth to her breast, I suppose. When I came to, she was in a mammoth rage, part cornered lioness, part heartsick lover. She pushed me off her, stood, and hurried to the medicine cabinet. A wind surged over the house, followed by a rattling hail. Julie charged out of the bathroom and threw my empty medicine bottle at me. "Bipolar loser!" she screamed. "Manic-depressive fuck! What are you thinking!"

She ordered me from the house, our house, her house. I was too confused and groggy to argue. Besides, anywhere I lived, in time, turned out not to be my home. I grabbed my shirt, shoes, and the medicine bottle and held them. If she hit me, would a bone crack open my face? Ice battered against the windows and thundered down on the roof. "Your father's son!" Julie said, and she looked ready to cry now. "Come back when you've got your head screwed on straight."

I waited on the porch until the storm had passed, then I tied my shoes (no socks), walked to the road, and started on my rueful way toward town, hailstones breaking beneath my feet. My thoughts were quick and fleeting as field mice darting for cover from out of a gray rain. My hands shook but my legs moved me forward well enough. I walked and waited for calm to catch up with me.

The railroad bridge—was that my real destination? I'd just as soon forget the pharmacist in town with his blazing eyes and smug compassion, his corporate voodoo pills meant to flatten my emotional life and help me to feel nothing, good or bad, for weeks. Instead I would go to the bridge, a haunted, vaulted piece of architecture in the middle of our nowhere, steeped in its own unique and troubling history. History by its very nature is *something*. Built high across the river, with cold, rusted steel tracks that rambled across the thick wooden support beams, it was an outdated bridge, some said, and dangerous, although no one ever did much to change the situation. People were drawn to the bridge because of that danger, often crossing it on foot and frequently at night, staring down into the river, tossing into their perplexed reflections their secret mistakes and grievances: letters from illicit lovers, tarnished wedding rings from failed or aborted marriages, a bloody knife, once a baby. Or an eyewitness thought she saw a baby dropped into the murky depths, although in truth the child turned out to be unwashed baby clothes and soiled diapers tied together in a deceptive knot.

Once, from the bridge, a vet drunk on wine and delusions fired a gun three times into the air. The bullets must have rained to earth somewhere, but no man or animal turned up suspiciously dead or wounded, so the vet woke in the morning on the floor of his trailer instead of a jail cell.

In certain moods I could picture myself pacing beneath the bridge during the fateful moment when the vet shot off his gun. Probably he confused that gun with the one he'd used during the war. A war gun and a handgun only appear to be different. In my vision, I'm walking beneath the bridge, listening to the voices rising off the river, when I hear a popping sound and a rush of wind that I mistake for my own indrawn breath. A bullet pierces my shoulder or else lodges far into my chest. Yet I keep walking. I'm one of those people who would try to ignore this improbable thing that has just happened, and in that way make it vanish. I would try not to notice the hot lacquer of blood seeping into my shirt, hoping that physical matter might have only what power we allow to it.

A woman I knew vaguely lost her life on the bridge. Her name had been Gloria, or maybe Gertie. She was balanced on the edge of one of the wooden guardrails, arms spread out in the way of a tightrope walker, when an unscheduled train pummeled by and shook her off. Or so the story goes. Dress ballooning over her head, G. dropped straight and steely quiet as an unsheathed knife into the water and disappeared. Why she was standing on the guardrail no one knows, but I would swear on what few beliefs I have left that it was not for the obvious reason. We met, in fact, when we both worked evening shifts on a suicide prevention hotline. This had been a couple of years ago, when I still thought I had enough inside me to give back to the less fortunate. During those last days before we were let go, she answered the phone something like this, "Suicide hotline, this is G. I'm divorced, I have shit for money, my husband slept with the judge and got the kids, I've a lump on my left breast you could bounce quarters off, and Meredith Baxter *still* refuses to play me in the TV movie. But tell me, what's on your mind?"

Yet the drunken vet, the doomed woman . . . neither of these sad people is the real story I meant to tell, which is what happened to the cows, and how I didn't hear or witness the accident that doomed so many of them. I was on the road that sharply curved before it ran under the bridge, and so should have at least heard what I wasn't in a position to see: the wheels grinding against the tracks when the brakes were pressed hard, for example, or boxcars colliding against the guardrails. That's yet another thing to fear—the magnitude of what you can miss when you're not paying attention and let your mind stray. Maybe I was looking down at the hailstones beneath my feet, or else I was gazing toward the sky where the summer ice had been just minutes before it shook to earth to rouse me from my bed of awkward sleep. I knew that science existed to explain how air could hold ice in the clouds over our heads, but even that word, science, and every mystery it entailed, burned inside my brain like sulfur.

Such was the state of my thoughts when I rounded the road's crooked curve, looked in front of me, and saw with my own naked eyes what I'm now about to tell you.

Train wreck! I shouted to myself, and for a moment everything seemed so astonishingly clear I didn't trust what I was seeing. The back end of the train had derailed off the tracks and crashed through the guardrail from which G. had fallen. One boxcar hung tilted off the bridge, suspended snakelike in air and pointed down toward the water. Two of the rear boxcars had detached from the snake tail altogether and dropped into the river, twisted, wrecked things that bobbed now on the water's surface, momentarily defying the laws of gravity by remaining afloat, something we all try to get by with from time to time. At first I thought those were people fallen from the train cars and thrashing with such fear in the river. But when you looked closer, you could see they were cows.

A couple dozen cows, it seemed, maybe more, the animals lurching against each other as they struggled against the rank green waves. Dazed and wide-eyed, they lifted their heads above the water and began to call out, frantic, impossible cries that were enough to raise the hair off a better man's arms.

I walked to the edge of the river. No one was around but me. Apparently everyone had some other place to be: working, planning, laughing, loving. I looked up at the train wreck teetering on the bridge, hoping for someone to take charge. From the steaming front boxcar a man in a flattened conductor's hat stepped out, clutching his forehead, a skinny thread of blood spreading from behind one ear. I couldn't have said how I knew about the blood, since my vision was not strong enough to see from such a distance.

Was it the knowledge of this man's injury, his inability to help, that propelled me to hurl myself with idiot passion into the river and start swimming out to the cows? The river was cold; my body jolted from the shock; even as I swam against the current, I was pretty sure this was not what I'd meant to do. This was no moral decision, my leap into the river, make no mistake. But once in the water, it seemed I'd committed to something and shouldn't turn back, and so did my actions, at that point, become infected with moral judgment?

A handful of the cows had been killed in the fall, and these were the ones I had to swim around, their motionless bodies like slabs of flotsam as they drifted down the current. I swam into the churning edge of the living cows, some of the most wounded bleeding crimson into the water.

What I planned was to help boost the cows back into the boxcars, one by one, until true help arrived. I couldn't see, at first, the absurdity of this idea. I swam to the nearest boxcar and clung to the door, but it began to rock back and forth and moan with the sound metal makes when being crushed under a trash compactor. I understood then that the whole car was sinking. Inside, a single young steer with an M branded into its side shivered in the far corner, possibly thinking he'd escaped the grim fate of his brethren cattle. When he saw me he stomped his hoof and shook his head of budding horns at the open door where I glowered in at him.

Water began to flood inside. I reversed my initial plan to load the cows into the boxcar and called upon the remaining cow to join us in the gory river. "Over here!" I yelled, slapping a dry spot of floor with the flat of my hand. "Here, boy!"

This was not your well-kept train car. Spread about were clumps of mulch and hay, shriveled cigarette butts, an empty barrel with a hole shot in its center, a sheet of newsprint (the president and a Chinese dignitary shook hands and stared out at me with a smugness peculiar to men who only have the world's problems on their minds), and cow shit around which flies still swirled in black buzzing cyclones. "Come on," I said aloud, because I had no other words or appeal with which to summon the animal and convey the urgency of his situation. I stooped to mental telepathy in a final attempt to get the animal to understand I was his single remaining hope. But with the boxcar capsized and flooding, the cow lost his balance and dropped to the floor, bawling at me—me!—like I was responsible for upending his world. "Fuck you!" I said loud enough for the cow to hear. I wanted to hurt that cow, insult him. Yet as I swam away before the sinking car could drag me under, I was on the verge of tears for having failed to win him over. Clearly he trusted his doom more than he trusted me, his clumsy and heedless would-be savior.

Back into the midst of the drowning cows I swam, an agitated vortex of floundering, belching animals. The air stank with the collective breath of their panicked cries. I thought I might start bellowing myself, and that would be fatal. A man's yell can slide as easily into madness as his silence. I have seen and heard this happen: a father, a brother, a woman who lived next door to me when I was a boy. One day she ran naked down the street with her pointed breasts painted pink, holding over her head a newspaper story about the clubbing of baby seals off the coast of Alaska. "This is the color of their slaughter!" she cried. "This is the color of a mother's pain! We are all of us pink on the inside, all of us, pink!" Eventually men on behalf of a psychiatric ward came to speak to her. They draped a colorless blanket over her shoulders and flaming breasts and lured her into the van that would deliver her for "examination."

Some cows were still tethered together, wet ropes strangling them as they struggled and pulled in opposite directions. My weak shaky arms couldn't snap the damned cords and heroically free them. I reached for the rope around the nearest cow's neck, my hair dripping stinging river water into my eyes, all the while thinking I could usher the cow toward shore and somehow inspire the confused herd to follow me. But he would not meet me halfway, not that cow, maybe a stubborn brother to the steer who had gone down with the boxcar. When I tugged at the rope, he bared his row of yellow skeptical teeth and bit my hand.

A couple of the more powerful cows broke free of the frenzied ring of us and began to cow paddle for shore. In their haste they swam over a struggling half-grown calf and pushed it under. When the calf surfaced it sneezed river bile and barked in desperation. I swam over to the calf, cradled my arms around its trembling body, and held on. None of the other cows mattered to me now. Let them care for themselves, senseless and inane creatures, bred to be fattened, slaughtered, and then eaten, as chilling a reason to exist as any I was likely to dream up for myself. But *this* cow I could manage, *this* was the one I could make live again.

Only the calf, too, fought against my every wretched attempt to save him. He kicked his hooves against my ribs, which sent the both of us briefly underwater, man and dumb cow, or was it cow and dumb man? For a moment we floated together in the belly of the river's current, and I intuited more than clearly saw what lay at the bottom of the river: a disembodied car door and a fender or two, empty oil cans, coiled fishnet, bony fish carcass, rocks fuzzy with gray mold, a man's wasted jeans, a woman's wig undulating like an exotic sea creature, books whose insights had maddened some redneck or maybe some scholar. My imagination delved deeper still, to G.'s shrunken corpse forever tangled in a nest of brush and seaweed, the water having moldered the dress from her starved body long ago.

When the calf and I tried to rise to the surface, the hoof of a thrashing cow above us caught me on the back of the skull. I felt something loosen inside my head, a knot unraveling and breaking open, then memories flooded into my consciousness, a torrent of fractured images assaulting me. I saw the forest of dark trees that ran all the way into our backyard where we lived when I was young, woods on one side and town on the other, a collision of civilization and country. But it isn't there, not in that yard, where a preacher kneels beside me and presses against my forehead a little cross that still hangs around his neck, as if I'm a young vampire who doesn't yet require a stake in the heart to keep in check. "There, don't you feel better?" he says and grips my shoulder, the cigarette smell of his hand taking on the stench of burned flesh and damnation.

A different hand now, a clenched hand. The fist opens and in my father's feverish palm lies an ancient pointed stone. It's hot from his touch alone. He unearthed this little relic, this gem, or so he claims, from a dirt pile in the backyard. "An Ojibway arrowhead," he says, and holds it to the light, although it looks like nothing other than run-of-the-mill stone. He wipes the arrowhead off with his shirttails and presents it to me as a gift. "For peace of mind," he says. "It doesn't come to you any other way."

My brother's voice at night from across the hall, I hear how his voice severs the darkness, words with the flat hiss of steam: "You sure you want to invest in what he believes in?" And later, maybe years: "You won't catch my image in a puddle of water."

My brother is walking out in the drenching rain with his arm around Marie Cobble, who is older and always swinging her hips. He kisses her throat, her face, the both of them walking away from the house toward town, my brother professing his love, his devotion, any number of promises I can't hear or even imagine. She pretends indifference, but any fool can see what she feels for him.

A strap of Marie's blouse loosens and slides down one arm, briefly revealing a rash of half-healed welts across her shoulders. What day is this, where are my brother or my parents? Where are we, Marie and I? We exist only in the vast featureless space of my own recall, so there is nothing but her shoulders and the way she stares at me staring at her pox of bruises. How did they get there, by who or what? They couldn't be self-inflicted, though most things are. The questions volley between us, unspoken but heard. At last she positions the strap back around her shoulder, covering the evidence, and flips me the bird for all I don't know.

Is that my mother gathering up the flowers that my father, in all his manic fury, has decapitated from their stems, every rose, tulip, lilac she was growing in the dirt beds around the house? She clutches them in her arms, all the shorn heads, and with her eyes dry, transports the broken flowers into the house and dumps them on the kitchen table, the smell of the rootless petals so sweet and oppressive I couldn't— wouldn't—breathe in their scent. I knew how the smell of them would kill me.

"Where are his *pills*?" my mother calls out from the bathroom, a different night, a different year, rifling through the box of Band-Aids, the Neosporin, the razor blades, the typical stock of a bathroom cabinet. "You know how he gets," she stage whispers to me. Only isn't *he* my brother this time, pacing the upstairs hall, crying that there's no sense in things, there's no sense in control, there is sense only in nonsense. He laughs bitterly, all the while ready to fly out of his own skin and torch the leftover carcass.

And there's the sound of a gun blasting off, the unmistakable sound a gun makes when it's being held to the side of your father's head. On this day or this year I'm standing in the woods with my brother, each of us with an ax in our hand, when the gun blast echoes over the trees. My brother raises his ax and I think he means to bury it in my skull or scalp me as a way to relieve his sudden panic and fear. Instead he curses and buries the ax in the trunk of the nearest tree. We run breakneck toward the house, me still holding the weight of my ax, the both of us following that echo even when we know in our souls what it means.

And later still, when we've returned from my father's funeral, my mother sprawls across the bed in her crumbled black dress and won't speak a word. Words, what do they matter, dead linguistic shells of sound? A whole paroxysm of words couldn't save him. A neighbor woman is seated next to her, stroking her shoulders, feeding her a couple of blue tablets. "Sweetheart," the woman says to me as I stand in the doorway, this woman whose name I no longer remember. "Sweetheart," she says, "remember none of this."

All these shards of my past ricocheted through my head where they'd been clogged, some for more than twenty years, yet providing only a brush stroke of my life story, the connections unclear but the memories and emotional residue still inside me, shimmering alive. And it's from this life, these ragged experiences, that I'm expected to create a whole self? All of those people were missing from my life now, for one reason or another. I fought my way to the surface of the river with the calf, as much out of protest at the abrupt return of memory as anything else. I'm no masochist; how many times do I need to repeat myself?

When the calf and I broke our heads above water into the cool whistling air, I was floating on my back with the calf lifted above me in some strange imitation of a wrestling hold, as if I were trying to flip it over and pin him to the water's surface. The calf wheezed like a consumptive; I could feel its heart pumping and surging beneath my arms. I was through pleading with the petrified animal and meant to save it whether I was forced to break its back or my own to do so. I looped one arm around the calf's neck in a headlock, using my free arm to beat at the water and fight our way toward shore with the rest of the forward-seeking cows. To help in this effort I grabbed hold of the tail of one powerful Bessie in front of me. Let her do all the swimming and work. I wasn't too proud. Survival has nothing to do with pride. The ones who say otherwise are dead.

Bessie kicked around in the water to rid herself of my grip on her tail. One of her legs swung back and connected squarely against my shin, although I felt the pain shoot through my calf. My calf, I thought, that was a good one. What hilarity! I shouted mock laughter into the sky, but of course only the knot of people who had gathered on the bank of the river strove to hear me. They shouted to me support, instructions, maybe mockery. It sounded the same from where I was.

Still I hung on to that cow's tail all the way to the shallows and dragged the calf with me. I rose from the river sputtering and rasping, a bull ready to charge. I'd never felt so energized or so exhausted. I released the calf and he stumbled away from me, choking, which was how I would have stumbled away from me if given the choice. No heartfelt bleat of goodbye from him or friendly swat on the butt from me. Yet this felt like a victory, or what I'd imagined over the years that victory must feel like. The feeling lasted for a moment or two and then faded away. The calf joined the circle of dripping cows that had gathered on a patch of riverside grass. Now that they were safe, they gazed with bovine calm at the river where the bodies of several cows still floated in the bloody water, then turned to us and yawned and shook themselves.

The conductor with the flattened cap made his way over to me, followed by a man who had apparently pulled off the side of the road on his way to somewhere else. He looked pitilessly strong and un-complicated in his jeans and spotless T-shirt, and was additionally blessed with medical knowledge of some sort. He checked my furious pulse and touched my cow-bruised ribs for broken bones. A woman stood behind the man, massaging sunscreen into her arms although the sun was not shining and the sky was still adrift with clouds. She was young and healthy and indifferent. I unreasonably wanted her in my life.

"Man, what were you doing out in the water?" the conductor asked. He removed his cap and held it to his somewhat concave chest, then tried to punch the cap back into shape, treating us to the momentary shiny luster of his scalp. The little stream of blood leaking from his ear was already beginning to dry. "That's just crazy, what you done, that's no way to be a hero."

The young man sat me on the ground and thumped my back, urg-ing my head between my legs until I coughed up a dark slippery spasm of water. My lungs were afire, burning like flame to an oil slick, accepting oxygen only painfully. My skin burned too, but it wasn't the kind of burning you could relieve through simple scratching. My head felt fattened from where I'd been kicked and my body hurt in most places, from the beating the cows had given me and from the exertion of swimming out to the middle of the river and back again. I was shaking, too, but that had nothing to do with physical pain. I glanced up toward the bridge where the train still hung, absurdly smashed, but it hurt my eyes to look at it now.

"Is he drowned?" the woman asked, but the conductor didn't seem to care as much about my welfare as he did trying to fathom the logic of my actions. "Them cows are going to the slaughterhouse anyway," he said. "Don't you see, trying to save them means nothing in the long run. They're dead or they're dead."

"The river's filthy," the woman observed while she admired her lotioned arms. "You have no idea what menace you could have exposed yourself to. Hepatitis or tetanus…"

I heard their dull human voices push against my ears but I couldn't care about what they said. Even the woman had already ceased being attractive to me. Instead my attention was riveted on the cows, huddled together as they were, grazing or nudging and sniffing one another. The calf had wandered over to an outcropping of rock and was licking it for salt—I guess for salt, but who knew what he really tasted? Every one of those cows thought he was safe, that the ordeal was already behind him. I tell you I envied them, their stupidity and blind oblivion, which protected them from seeing how the chaos of the last few minutes, for all of us, had only just begun.

Christmas morning in Mobile, Alabama, 1979. That's my older
sister Monica as Supergirl. Misty's the confused child in knee socks,
aka Wonder Woman. I'm the modest Batgirl in roller skates.

Michelle Richmond is the author of the novel *Dream of the Blue Room* (2003),
and *The Girl in the Fall-Away Dress* (2001), a collection which won the AWP Award
for Short Fiction. A native of Alabama and a former James Michener Fellow, she
lives in Northern California and teaches in the MFA program in writing at the
University of San Francisco. Her stories and essays have appeared in a number of
literary journals and anthologies.

THE HERO OF
QUEENS BOULEVARD

Michelle Richmond [signature]

Michelle Richmond

I've been having these egg-headed thoughts about non-linear time and a parallel universe. It's been going on for twenty years, and lately they've been coming between me and my wife. My wife believes in one world, one time, one perfect moment. My wife believes in making the decision, because, she says, looking up from the PBS documentary *Life of Baby*, "Right now is all we've got." I'm standing on the fire escape of our one-bedroom sublet at 85th and Columbus, working the grill, conversing with her through the open window. She's rubbing her belly in a wistful manner. There's this baby on the TV screen, newly delivered, a tiny glistening bundle, and my wife is looking at this baby like it is just about the most beautiful thing on the planet.

My wife defends murderers for a living, and she means it when she says that stuff about right now. One minute you're buying beaded purses from a vendor on 34th Street, and the next, poof, you're dead on the stairwell, skirt hiked above your knees, neck twisted in an unnatural way, a black cord around your throat, some guy's wet dream. Sometimes at night she brings her work home, spreads photographs of the victims across the kitchen table and studies them, trying to figure out why, given the evidence, her guy can't be connected beyond a shadow of a doubt to this particular body. Sometimes, out of grotesque curiosity, a fascination with the horror that is my wife's bread and butter, I glance at the photos, which more often than not make my stomach turn, and I wonder what kind of bastard could do that. Then I'll look at my wife looking at the photographs, lost in thought, her long brown hair trailing the table, her quick fingers tracing the shape of a corpse, and I'll think, this is my wife, who believes there are no absolutes.

"Just look," she says now, pointing at the newborn, which has somehow been transformed and is swaddled up like the baby Jesus, all clean and pink, resting in its mother's arms. While the camera was covering the lower regions, somebody thought to put orange lipstick on the mother, who now lies there, staring alternately at the baby and the camera, making kissy faces. Then the camera pans to the husband, who is also making kissy faces, and my wife looks at me as if I'd just strangled a kitten or been caught with a hooker. "Some men *want* to be fathers," she says.

My first instinct is to be mad, but then I see that she's crying, and to top it off she's trying to hide it. The only thing worse than my wife crying is my wife trying to pretend she isn't crying, or maybe, come to think of it, Mrs. Shevardnadze, our upstairs neighbor, leaning out her window and shouting, "I'm going to call the fire department on you!" which is exactly what she's doing right now.

Then my wife stops pretending she isn't crying, she just lets it all go, so I shut the lid on the grill and climb through the window and sit on the couch beside her and put my arms around her and say, "Baby, I'm just not ready."

"What's there to be ready for?" she says. "You and that dialectic philosophy."

She says "dialectic" like it's a dirty word, half whisper, half curse. She's good at bandying the term about, but she doesn't buy it—the connection between dialectic philosophy and my fear of procreation. She likes to say I flunked out of the Study of Either-Or, and I like to remind her that I didn't flunk out—I dropped out, and there's a big difference. One year away from a Ph.D. at what is often referred to as a venerable institution, and something happened. I didn't lose interest, exactly. I didn't lose faith. I just couldn't bring myself to open another scholarly journal. When I sat down at my computer to work on my dissertation, more often than not I ended up playing solitaire, or opening the "outdated correspondence" file on my hard drive, reading old letters I wrote years ago to girlfriends whose faces I couldn't exactly remember.

"I can't do this," I said ten years ago, looking at pages and pages of small text scattered across my desk, the floor, the kitchen table. The truth was I had outdone myself. The more complex my argument became, the less I understood. I began to feel I was losing my grasp of the subject. All the threads were coming apart.

"So don't," she said.

Case closed. We got married in the Hamptons, where her parents had a place, and I became a high-school teacher. My wife became, over time, a high-powered defense attorney. She gets people off the hook for crimes they may or may not have committed.

"But what if he's guilty?" I sometimes ask, standing over her at the kitchen table while she reads through stacks of legal documents. "What's guilty?" she says. "Aren't we all guilty? Is anyone really guilty? Guilty's a matter of perspective, just varying shades of gray."

Which is where we diverge wholeheartedly. I believe in black and white. Guilty or innocent. You love someone or hate her. I'm not ashamed to confess that I swallowed all that stuff hook, line, and sinker back in college—how the universe is made up of polar opposites battling against each other, how this constant conflict between good and evil, light and dark, fuels the whole world. My belief in that system never wavered, and this is at the root of my problem with babies.

A man can be either a good father or a bad one. I had a good one. My wife had a bad one. And if I were forced to choose dialectically my own fatherly potential—whether I'd be good or bad—I can't say how I'd vote. I've tried to explain that to my wife—how, until I can know with one hundred percent certainty that I would make a good father, I can't bring myself to be one. This, to me, seems fair.

"That's ridiculous," she says. "You're building a trap. You can't know until you try. But you won't try until you know. Just admit it. You hate kids."

"Not true," I say. "If I didn't like kids, would I be a teacher?"

She goes into the bedroom and slams the door. I can smell the steaks burning on the fire escape. Mrs. Shevardnadze is stomping around upstairs. Some kids are rapping on the street below. The M-11 rattles by. It's May, so the alley below our window smells like dog piss.

I teach at a prep school for boys out on the island. For years I've been lobbying the Curriculum Development Committee for a class in dialectic philosophy, but each year they refuse, labeling such modes of thinking outdated and irrelevant. So I teach American History, European Wars, and Intro to Philosophy, coach water polo, and every now and then the headmaster railroads me into moderating the chess team, even though I can't remember the last time I won a game of chess. I feel ill at ease with the other teachers, who all have masters degrees in education—and who seem to believe that teaching is a calling, rather than an accidental vocation. My own aborted Ph.D in philosophy feels somehow inadequate. Sometimes in the teachers' lounge the other faculty talk about pedagogical theory, or about the spiritual rewards of teaching, and I just dig into my burrito and look down at a stack of papers, pretending to prepare for class.

But one day a year, things are different. One day a year I get to teach dialectic philosophy, and that's when I really come into my own. This year, my big day happens to fall in the same week as the baby argument.

So it's the morning after the big fight, 6:30, and I'm driving to work. I want to get there early. Usually I make the trip in a zombie state, but today, I'm totally awake. I'm feeling good, really confident, thinking about how I'm going to explain dialectic philosophy to my students, how I'm going to shake them out of their indifference. Usually this drive just kills me, because Queens Boulevard goes on forever. You might as well be driving across Europe or Asia, the boulevard's so diverse. One minute you feel like you're in China, the next you're in the Middle East, at some point you hit the good old U.S. of A. The girls walking to school in their miniskirts and platform shoes look like they know a great deal more at sixteen than you'll ever know in a lifetime. Today I'm cruising through every light, one green signal after another, and I'm not even surprised, because this is the day I hit my stride, my one day a year, and you better believe the universe is working in my favor.

As I'm coming up to 42nd the green clicks over to yellow, and half a second later it's red, and I'm sitting here, slightly perturbed at this unexpected intrusion on my perfect morning, but still feeling good, because it's just one light and it'll be over with before the optimistic guy on the radio finishes predicting sunshine. It's 6:45 in the morning but the taxis are already out in full force, the newspaper stands are open; all along the boulevard people are stepping out of shops and apartment buildings with paper and brief case in one hand, coffee in the other. It's noisy as hell, like it always is on Queens Boulevard, but today I don't so much mind the noise because it's just background music for the lecture I'm playing in my head. There are four lanes on this boulevard, all going one direction, my direction, and I'm in the fourth lane from the morgue, which is what I call this massive rectangular building made entirely of pocked gray cement that spans the length of an entire block. The building has not a single window. The subway cars run on top of it. Where Queens Boulevard intersects 42nd, a bridge arches over the street, and below the bridge is a tunnel.

So I'm sitting at the light, and I'm watching the E train go by on my left, passing over the morgue, across the bridge, and onward. It's moving along at a pretty good pace, but I can still see the sad, sleepy faces of the people going to work. And that's when I hear the screeching. You know the arc of a screech, how it begins at a high pitch, becomes even louder and higher, then somehow winds down as the moving vehicle slows, then comes to a halt. So I've got my ears tuned in and I'm listening for the wind-down, but it doesn't come; the screeching just suddenly stops, and I know something's wrong. Just then I see something coming out of the tunnel—not just anything, but a Jeep, and it is literally flying, four feet off the road and wheels to the sky, and it's not headed in just any direction. It's headed straight for me.

But what is more alarming, perhaps, than the aborted screech and the upside-down flying Jeep and the horrified faces of the people on the street, is the speed at which all this is happening. The Jeep isn't flying so much as it is hovering. The whole thing is happening in slow motion. The flying Jeep, the passing E train, the pedestrians on every side of me, are moving at a fraction of their regular speed, and here's the rub: I happen to be switched into fifth gear. While the rest of the world goes freeze frame, my brain is clicking along faster than it ever has before. As the Jeep gets closer I'm planning my next move, which is to get out of my own car, which I do, and the Jeep's still coming, and it's only about six feet from me now. The Jeep drops out of the air, skids another few feet on its roof, and stops inches from my car. And I'm thinking about how I've never been prepared in my life, not once, and as I'm moving toward the Jeep, I'm seriously doubting that this is what I should be doing, thinking maybe I should let someone else do it instead, because, let's face it, I don't know the first thing about car crashes—like how to open a jammed door, or how to tell if the thing's about to blow.

So I'm jogging over to the car, sort of a fake jog because what I'd really like is for someone else to take over. But no one else is moving. In addition to the screech there was, at the moment the Jeep landed, a sickening crunch, and now everyone is looking alternately at me and at the Jeep, and waiting for something to happen. I experience what I can only describe as a moment of clarity. For the first time in my life I have in front of me a purpose with which I cannot argue, a clear course of action.

Suddenly there is a strange coolness on my nose, and the coolness is the glass of the back window of the Jeep against which my nose is pressed, and someone is looking at me. It is a girl of about five, maybe six. This girl is hanging upside down, suspended in the Jeep's interior, her small bright body held fast in a car seat. Quite clearly she is surprised, and she is waiting for something. No, she isn't just waiting for something, she's waiting specifically for *me*, and because my mind is working at about ten times its normal speed while the rest of the world inches forward like an ice floe, I know she is waiting to be rescued. I open the door, which opens more easily than one would expect, and I say, "Don't worry, sweetheart." Very carefully I unbuckle

the car seat with one hand while supporting the child with the other—
I can do this because she is very light. I am struck in fact by how light
a five-year-old girl can be; she is not much heavier than the blue-
gray cat I reluctantly share with my wife. I take her out of the car and
stand her upright, and she says, "Where is my lunchbox? I lost my
Peoples of the World lunchbox." I look inside for the lunchbox. A
woman in the front seat turns and says to me, "Good morning."

"Hello, ma'am." I immediately regret calling her ma'am, since she's
no older than I am.

The lunchbox is lying on the ceiling of the Jeep within easy grasp.
I pick it up and hand it to the girl. This lunchbox has drawings of
people of different colors and sizes and facial shapes; secretly I ap-
plaud the artist who is spreading such good vibes to the children of
this great and ridiculous city through the overlooked medium of lunchbox art. Standing there with her brown curly hair arranged quite
properly, her lunchbox clutched in her tiny fingers, and her face a bit
cross, this child looks like any five- or six-year-old girl on her way to
school with her Peoples of the World lunchbox, and not one bit like
a child who has just flown upside down in a Jeep through a tunnel
and been rescued by a stranger in a stupid red baseball cap that he
wears every time he teaches dialectic philosophy.

Then it occurs to me that a) my work is not done, b) having saved
the child, the logical next step is to save the mother, and c) the rest of
the world still seems stunned into inaction. I walk quickly but not
too quickly—I do not want to inspire panic in the child—to the
other side of the car, where the woman is hanging upside down in
front of the steering wheel. Her hair is very short. I open the door.
"How is my daughter," the woman says. She says it as a simple com-
mand, unquestionably authoritative, although her voice is a bit shaky.

"Your daughter is standing over there. She's all right."

She blinks once. "Okay," she says. Her eyes are extraordinarily green,
so green that they cannot possibly be natural. For a moment I am in
love with her, but the feeling quickly passes.

"Could you please place your hands on the ceiling," I say, "like
you're doing a hand stand. I don't want you to fall on your head." She

does so, and I unbuckle her seat belt, being careful not to brush up against any places that she might not, for reasons of modesty, want me to brush up against. Then I help her crawl out of the car, and she goes around to her daughter and tucks her daughter's shirt into her bright overalls, and the two of them sit down on the sidewalk.

Suddenly, the second hand moves forward, the minute hand clicks into place, and real time is restored. "Mrs. Fernandez," a boy is saying. The boy is about fourteen and he is wearing an orange vest and holding one of those signs that says *Slow Children Playing*. "Mrs. Fernandez, it's me, Jose, the crossing guard. Are you okay?"

Mrs. Fernandez looks up at Jose. "Oh," she says. "It's you. Hon, have you seen my dog?"

Just then a woman in a svelte black suit and smart heels walks up. She is one of those New York City women who could be anywhere between twenty-five and forty-seven years old, and who would be wearing a svelte black suit at any hour on any day; one of those women who I am not the least bit surprised to see clutching a rather large black lab to her chest at 6:49 on a Monday morning. This woman's hair is long and perfect. It shines alluringly in what passes for sunlight on this rather dismal morning. This woman's hair is, in fact, the exact same color as the dog's coat—and it strikes me that this is a skill that only this very particular type of New York City woman has—the ability to pick up a dog that has just been tossed violently from a moving vehicle and make it look like a well-planned accessory. She walks up to Mrs. Fernandez and says, "Is this your dog, Miss? Is this black lab the dog you are looking for?"

"Oh yes, thank you," says Mrs. Fernandez.

The whole street has sprung into action now. There are suddenly a great number of pedestrians crowded around Mrs. Fernandez and her well-adjusted daughter, and they are all very concerned, and at least a dozen of them are dialing 911 on their cell phones. I walk back to my car, which is blocking an entire lane, and of course the lane is backed up and the light is green and a lot of people are honking at me. The whole thing has taken no more than three rotations of the light.

I pull away. I go to school. I give a brilliant lecture. And then, standing there in my red baseball cap, right in the middle of my brilliant lecture, I begin to doubt dialectic philosophy. I begin to sense this gray area, in which things do not have to happen one way or the other: you do not either love someone or hate her, you do not necessarily play either the hero or the fool, you are not either a great or terrible father. A new possibility occurs to me, the possibility that, in each case, the truth lies somewhere in between. Is it possible that the accident had nothing at all to do with a parallel universe? Is it possible that, at the moment the Jeep came hovering out of the tunnel, I did not click over into some hitherto hidden world in which I behaved in a manner exactly opposite to how I would expect myself to behave? Could it be that my heroic actions on Queens Boulevard are a true representation of the man I am, and that, until now, I simply have not been tested? I have always considered myself to be a man lacking courage and conviction, but perhaps I never before encountered the appropriate situations. Is it possible that, all these years, I have insisted upon a parallel universe as a sort of crutch, a rationale for all my own weaknesses. "Yes," I say. "Here, today, I am like *this*, but in that other universe, the mirror opposite of this one, I am courageous, decisive, brilliant, witty, entertaining, compassionate, extraordinarily good looking, and, above all, virile."

I look out at my students and sense their excitement waning, expressions of intense boredom settling across their faces. Before, I was the quintessential evangelist, converting new followers simply by the strength and fury of my conviction. My students were swept up in my passion, transfixed, awestruck. Today is different. The bell rings. I am standing with chalk in hand, arm raised high, extolling a philosophy which suddenly seems flawed, when my students breathe an audible and collective sigh of relief, scramble out of their seats, and rush for the door.

I leave school immediately after the final bell. Driving home along Queens Boulevard, I scan the scene for the next debacle—hovering Jeeps, stranded motorists, dogs lost in traffic—my next golden opportunity. But the drive is uneventful. Back home, my wife is sitting at the kitchen table, the latest scene of murder spread out before her—a young victim with haunting eyes, a silver pendant dangling primly from her bruised neck. "The Pendant Murders," my wife says matter of factly, canvassing the photo with her magnifying glass. I step too close to the table and see a little more of the picture than I want to. The girl is blonde and thin, and her turtleneck has been cut open at the top, her throat slashed. A silver pendant dangles from her neck. The pendant is a tiny half-moon with a jewel at its center.

Beside the photos is the evening edition of the *Daily News*. My wife prefers the *Times*, makes fun of the fact that I subscribe to the sensational *Daily News*, but I have always been comforted by its simplicity, its ability to see everything in terms of black and white. The *Daily News* lacks the muddle and grind of complexity, uncertainty, weighing of the facts. Hillary is a queen one day, a pariah the next, but never in between. I also like the visual presentation. Every day there is a huge headline, seventy- or eighty-point type, over an eye-catching photo. Today, the photo reveals the blurry shape of a man in jeans and a baseball cap. His back is to the camera, and he is leaning into a Jeep, which is upside down on a busy road. Beside him on the street, looking into the camera, is a small girl in crumpled overalls. In the front seat of the Jeep there is an upside-down woman, who seems to be saying something to the man. In the photo it looks as if, having saved the child, the man is having a conversation with the mother, probably telling her not to panic, not to move her head, probably asking her appropriate questions, such as, "Can you feel your toes? Are you dizzy? Is your vision blurred?" What I know, of course, is that the man in the baseball cap is not saying anything medically sound to the woman; he is simply retrieving the child's Peoples of the World lunchbox. The headline reads, "Who Is the Hero of Queens Blvd?"

I say to my wife, "Did you see the paper?"

"Yep. The usual stuff. Man saves mother and child from certain disaster."

"You're a cynic."

"Actually, I admire him." She puts down her magnifying glass and glances at the paper. "Cute girl," she says. Then she looks at me accusingly, the way she did when she saw the father holding the infant on

Life of Baby, the way she does whenever a friend of hers gets pregnant.

"I'll be in the bedroom," I say.

"It's only four o'clock."

"Like I said, I'll be in the bedroom."

A few minutes later, she's there, and her red summer dress is draped across the rocking chair, and she is opening the drawer of the bedside table, reaching for the condom, and I close the drawer and say, "Never mind that," and her mouth is open in a slight and endearing way, and her neck is pale and convincing, and I am Parallel Lover, a new and much-sought-after superhero—intense and nurturing, generous and rabid, strong and gentle, impeccable.

The sheets are askew. The room is hot. Down below, the phonograph man rattles by, the thick delicious sound of blues drifting up from his cart. Mrs. Shevardnaze is screaming at her cat. The pigeons on the eaves are cooing. My wife's breathing, finally, has slowed. Her eyes are closed, her hand draped lightly over my thigh. She looks more at peace than I've ever seen her.

Soon, she is asleep and smiling slightly, unaware that I am watching. In her dreams, perhaps the dead girls are receding. For a few hours, at least, she will forget the Pendant Murders; for a few hours the world will seem like a bright, inviting place. I too am willing to believe this, am willing to believe that, at this very moment, there is a tiny flame alight in the dark recesses of her womb. There, in that place so far from reach, it has already begun: a slow and certain growth, some tiny glistening thing.

*My mother tells me that I started speaking at a very early age
and she would often find me standing in a corner of my crib
talking to myself. When she asked me what I was doing
I would say that I was pulling a movie out of the wall.*

Robert Olen Butler has published ten novels, most recently *Fair Warning* (2002) and *Mr. Spaceman* (2000), and two volumes of short stories, one of which, *A Good Scent from a Strange Mountain*, won the 1993 Pulitzer Prize for Fiction. His new book of stories, *Had a Good Time*, based on his collection of antique picture postcards, will be published in August 2004. A recipient of both a Guggenheim Fellowship in fiction and a National Endowment for the Arts grant, he also won the Richard and Hinda Rosenthal Foundation Award from the American Academy of Arts and Letters, and a National Magazine Award for Fiction. He directs the Creative Writing Program at Florida State University.

HIRAM THE DESPERADO

Robert Olen Butler

Mr. O. E. Malsberry
Instrument man P. R. R.
Gorgona, C. Z. Panama

Dear Owen—This is the school where Cousin Hiram reigns supreme &
curries the town ruffians. All's well. Chas.

Postmarked Charleston, Wash.,
Apr. 24, 1908

Say, don't you think they need somebody to tell them what to do?
These kids all around me? Another kid to tell them, I mean. Me.
Not like the things they hear plenty of already. Elbows off the table
and quiet down and be in this room on that tick of the clock and add
up these meaningless numbers and eat your greens. But things that
have something to do with something. So for instance I tell the six-
and seven-year-olds to steal cigarettes for me from their dads, just one
every other day and only from a near-full pack, nothing the old man'll
even realize is gone, and for this I'll keep the big kids off their backs;
and then I tell the thirteen- and fourteen-year-olds not to rough up
the six- and seven-year-olds, and I keep them in cigarettes for going

along with it. I perform a service for everybody, and it has to do with what they really need, in this case protection and smokes. And sure, along the way in this one particular part of the doings, I keep a few extra cigarettes to smoke for myself and I get a few extra favors from the biggest of the older kids. That's only fair.

Say, we're just trying to get out of childhood in one piece, all of us. It's a new century, so they keep reminding us. There's some swell stuff going on. But I'm sitting around in a kid's body and I'm waiting for influenza and diphtheria and dengue fever and the black cholera and infantile paralysis, and if you go out to play, one of those swell automobiles will run you down or an aeroplane will crash on your barn with you in the hayloft or a sixteen-foot cedar-cut will roll off a logging sled and right over you or your dad will drink the whole pail full of beer in about one hour flat, not to mention half a bottle of whiskey, and he'll beat you near to death for breathing too heavy or you can get knuckled to death by anybody who happens to have been born a few years before you—they say kids have died having their brains scrambled up by a good knuckling to the temple while in a headlock—and there's always being bored to death sitting in a schoolroom all day with George Washington staring down from over the blackboard looking like he's as bored as you, not to mention a Sunday afternoon when it rains all get-out and you are doing so bad you still have your church-going collar on and no strength to even take it off, this Puget Sound rain is coming down so hard. Kids have been known to seize up and keel over dead sitting in a window seat or on a porch swing with the rain coming down on a Sunday afternoon.

The boy who moved in next door—he was twelve, same as me, though I never got a chance to play with him—had himself a growth on his neck. He was a Catholic and went to parochial and so he wasn't on display at our school, where we hadn't had a good goiter for several years, and I made better than a dollar selling a nickel view of him from our attic window, which could see down into his fenced backyard and him sitting there in the sun. Then last week he was gone and they put up the black wreath and I guess it was something worse than a goiter, and that kid didn't need anybody telling him to divide thirteen into a hundred and four or to sit up straight. I don't know what his dad was like.

So ain't I already saying how I can be fidgeting to death in a front desk of a classroom on a spring day that's working up to rain as soon as the bell rings? I'm not in that front desk out of choice or even the alphabet. I'm put there to be in knuckle-striking range and where I can't whisper worth a hoot or pass a note, and it's like that from the first day of class anymore, me being a known desperado. It's the price I pay. I saved others, but myself I couldn't save, which is one true thing, at least, that I learned while being brought to the brink of death-by-boredom at my weepy mother's side in church.

Anyways, I'm sitting there in school one day this spring and I can't find a place in that chair where my tail bone is happy about anything and there's a terrible itch in my left heel and digging at it with the toe of my right shoe isn't helping. Mrs. Pickernose is droning on about something—that isn't her real name, but I saw her with her finger up her nose once after school when she thought nobody was looking, and I'm still waiting to give out that information in some useful way sometime. But I'm sitting there when I see out the classroom door and Miss Spencer walks past.

Say, I can be in love, can't I? I don't have to explain any of that. If most of the hundred-something other boys in this school would ride me down the hill to Port Orchard Bay on a saw blade and dump me in if they figured I was mashed on a girl—not to mention a full-grown woman, not to mention a teacher—then that's just why I'm the guy who runs things and not them, because they're all a little backward, is how I see it, and I don't have to fess up to nothing, much less explain myself. Not that I ever got any advice about this sort of thing. Pa don't talk about nothing. The few boys who some girls think of as their beaus, they haven't got the first idea about it. It's something I just know to do. She's past that door in one second flat, but she's as clear as can be in my head. She's got her hair all twisted up in the back like that princess who Cupid was stuck on that's in our reader. Miss Spencer has never been my teacher, and I guess it's better that way, her not having a direct chance to think of me as rotten, though if she had to crack my knuckles with a ruler I'd be pretty happy just to have her thinking that strong about me at all.

This has been going on for a few months already. On this particular day, after the bell, I go out and she's walking away fast, her purse and her books tucked hard against her chest, and I follow her for about a quarter of a mile past the logger cut-off and she's still walking fast like she's got serious business downtown, but I've got things to do and I let her go.

I've only ever spoken a little bit to Miss Spencer. Once, she came upon me out back of school collecting dues from a mollycoddle who didn't understand the workings of the Grand Fraternal Lodge and Benevolent Association of Cedar Weevils.

"But when do we meet?" he says to me.

"We don't meet," I say.

"So why do I pay dues?" he says.

"Say," I say, "don't you have even a little sense? There's privileges."

"What sort?" he says.

I'm not quite ready to knuckle his brains. He's two years younger and kind of on the small side, and that's always a final argument, but I've found there are fewer problems if you use reasoning. "The secret handshake," I say, wiggling my fingers at him. "The code of honor. And ain't I letting you skip the terrors of initiation? Do you think a privilege like that ain't worth ten cents? What would your fellow Weevils think, them having paid up and also bearing the scars of the rites of initiation? You need to take into account how subject you could be to this and that."

Which is when Miss Spencer walks up, right as I'm doing a serious forefinger tap into the center of the kid's chest and he's finally getting that look in his eye like logic is going to prevail.

"Hiram," she says, and I didn't even realize that she knew my name.

I stuff my hands into my pockets and turn to her. Her face is swell, is all I can say.

"Are you playing rough with this little boy?" she says.

I smile slow. She knows my name but not his. "Not at all," I say. "We was just discussing."

"We *were* just discussing," she says, stressing the word I already knew

I got wrong. I'm not stupid. I pick up more than they realize. "And what might that be?" she says.

I say, "Oh, *this and that*," which the Weevil-to-be understands right off.

"This and that," he repeats, and I look at him and give him a very friendly nod. He gives me a nod back, like we understand each other. Miss Spencer made the mistake of calling him a "little boy," and that reminded him of who he really depends on. I even turn to him and grab his hand like I'm shaking it, but I sort of jiggle it around a few times right and left and he's beaming now with his first Weevil secret, he thinks, the handshake.

"That's all right then," Miss Spencer says.

I turn back to her, wanting the conversation to go on. I say, "Nice weather we're having, Miss Spencer, isn't it?"

She looks at me with just a little pinch in her forehead, like she's not sure she wants to talk about the weather to a kid. Then she says, "If you like rain."

"You're not used to rain?" I say, and I'm thinking what I've heard about her, which she now tells me.

"Last year I taught in California," she says. "It's very wet up here by contrast."

"That's what puts the *wash* in Washington," I say. I'm pitching like Christy Mathewson here, but she has to go.

"All right, boys," she says. "Be good."

"Sure," I say. And that's the longest conversation I've ever had with the woman I love.

So it's a couple hours later on the day when I follow her from school. It's working up to time for Pa to come home and I go into the kitchen and get the beer pail. It's sitting next to the door so I can just step in and take it without any talk. Ma is rolling out some dough and usually she's all over me about something I've done, but she acts like I'm not even there, which is how it goes at pail time.

I head on down the hill toward the bay and I can see the smoke-stacks of the *USS Iowa* in dry dock at the Navy Yard, which is pretty swell, and I dream a little about somehow having control of this view, and I'm selling admission and toting up dollar after dollar. I dream a little, too, about the Great White Fleet that our president has sent off to circle the world and show them all who's boss, sixteen battleships and six torpedo boats, and I feel bad for the *Iowa* that got left behind, it being a big hero in Cuba and all. Even battleships can get a raw deal. This all is what's going through my head with Pa's beer pail swinging in my hand, when I get down to Front Street and see Miss Spencer.

I've made the turn up toward the docks, heading for the saloon, and the trade's a little rough along here, and there she is, the last person I'd expect to be walking along. She's on the other side of the street heading the opposite direction from me, and at first all I see is her—there's nothing else on the street, or in the whole state of Washington for that matter—her in her white shirt waist and black skirt. Her face is lowered a little like she's concentrating on where she's walking, which is a pretty good idea around these parts, actually. Then I realize there's a guy at her side, a Navy guy in his blues. I don't know he's with her till I see them go a few steps and keep alongside each other. But she's not looking at him and he's not looking at her and they're not saying nothing. She'd have me put that different, I know. I'd always talk perfect around Miss Spencer, because I can if I want to, and it'd make her happy.

I think they're heading for the nickel motion-picture show up the street. But I don't like how her face is down and how they're acting. Something's wrong here. I cross the street and follow them. He's a little guy, not even quite as tall as Miss Spencer, which makes me real edgy inside, like this could be me beside her as likely as him. They pass the motion-picture show right by, and the brickyard, and they cut in at a footpath through the waterfront park. They circle the band stand and nothing's changed about how they're walking. There's a little space between them like they're trying not even to accidentally bump into each other, and there's no talking as far as I can tell, and she's still got her head down. Yet it's not like they've just met or something. There's a real familiar feel going on between them, too. Like you pick up from somebody's parents, my own Ma and Pa even, when she gets him to go off to church once in a while and I'm walking behind them. Finally Miss Spencer and her bluejacket slow and stop and they start to turn around to sit on a bench and I duck off the path and into some shrubs and crouch down and wait for them to get settled. A Port Orchard steamer out on the bay toots its whistle. Another couple walks by and the guy shoots me a look, and I'd give him a *Bugs* or a *Dry up* except I don't want to draw attention to myself. But even this dope has his girl's arm through his. Then I peek out at Miss Spencer and this guy she's spending time with who's maybe a problem for her.

They're sitting side by side all right, pretty close now, and he's talking and then she's talking, but they're not looking each other in the eye, and then they just sit for a while. I settle down where I am. I've got a Piedmont in my pocket and a dry match, and I light up and puff away. I don't look at the pail. I know it's there and time's passing and I'm going to catch something bad for doing this, but I'm not ready to leave Miss Spencer out here with this guy. Though I'm not looking at them, either. I'm just sitting in the middle and smoking a cigarette.

When I look at them again, they're just starting to stand up. One thing I notice. She puts her hand just below her stomach, but very light, like it hurts. I know right off what's been going on, like I knew the first time I saw them on the street. Pa's smart. He don't like me showing his handiwork, usually. Ma cares about that. She's got to tote me off to church and she don't want folks knowing how bad a boy I really am. When it's not a strap or a lath or a shake across the back of me from my collar to my shoes, it's a fist right where she's touching.

They're coming this way and I duck down and hunker into the bush. They could see me if they turn, but they don't. They drift past like a dark cloud and I wait a bit and I'm pretty angry and trying to think what to do to this guy. For now I follow them. And there's two more things I notice. On the footpath, with nobody around and Front Street coming up, he tries to take hold of Miss Spencer's hand and she jerks it away. That just shows me I'm right. And if he wants to get tough with her right here for taking her hand away, I'm ready to run up on him and do what damage I can with this pail across the side of his head and my fingers in his eyes and my teeth taking chunks out of his ears. But he doesn't do a thing. He keeps walking. Which figures.

It's a public place. Guys like this know how to keep it all private.

Then the other thing I notice comes a few minutes later, along Front Street. He tries to take her hand once more and she lets him. She holds his hand for a moment like it's still okay between them, and then they let go, but they move a little closer to each other as they walk.

Say, don't I know how that happens? Don't I realize I have to stop and let these two go on to wherever they're going, and don't I double back to my Pa's favorite saloon and go around to the back door? Some woman with a tired face is there ahead of me and she's just starting to move off with a pail of beer, and I guess she loves her man, and I'd rather do this myself than have Ma come down to Front Street every day. Fat Ed in his apron takes my pail, and he's okay, Fat Ed. He gives me a couple of cigarettes and a handful of radishes from the free eats and I pop the radishes on the way home and they're real good. They taste sharp, a little bitter, just what I need.

The next day the father of our country is watching me squirm to find a way to sit in my desk that don't hurt too bad, and he's not changing that little smirk on his face. Being father of the country, he had his hands full with all the backs to whip, I guess, about a million. So I keep my mind on what to do with this bluejacket who normally I'd think is pretty swell, him fighting for his country and having a swell uniform to show for it. But say, there's only so much you can allow somebody for being whatever else they are. The main thing is he's hurting Miss Spencer.

So I go to my two best hard-boiled eggs, a couple of fourteen year olds who I find smoking out over the knoll behind the school and who I've done some things for way beyond the Piedmonts they're sucking on right now. Joe's dad is a logger, and Joe's taller by a hand than the guy I'm after. Billy's only a little over my size, but he would bite an ear clear off if he needed to. I see their plumes of smoke and I come up over the knoll and they jump up fast from where they were crouching.

"Yay, Hiram," Joe says. "I thought you was a teacher."

"Yay, Joe," I say. "Yay, Billy."

"Yay, Hiram," Billy says.

"I may need another note from my mom soon," Joe says.

"You know where to come," I say. My handwriting is a lot better than any of the teachers realize. I say, "I need a favor from you, too. Both of you."

Joe lifts a clenched fist before his face. "You just point me," he says.

"Bet your knickerbockers," Billy says, lifting his own fist.

"Good men," I say. "Good men. And you're right about needing this." I lift my fist with theirs. "The three of us."

"We need to recruit some more Weevils?" Joe says.

"There's a sailor in town we've got to teach a lesson," I say.

The fists fall and the eyes widen. It's true this is nothing like what I've asked of them before. Or of myself, either.

"A *sailor*?" Joe says.

"An *adult*?" Billy says.

I don't need to listen to any more. I suddenly understand I'm standing here with children. I turn and head up over the knoll. "The note for my mom...," Joe calls after me.

Sailors drink. This is something I know. They get drunk and then they stagger around Front Street late at night. I'm a kid. I still look like one. Nobody notices a kid or thinks a kid can do certain things. I don't need some damn army of children crusaders with me to do what I have to for Miss Spencer. So my Pa has some old logging tools in the stable out back and I fetch his beer and tonight he passes out before he can get angry, which happens four nights out of five, to be honest, and Ma is passed out too, mostly from tiredness. I go to the stable and find me a billhook, which is just right, pretty short and easy to swing, but with a nasty curved blade. It still has a good gouging point to it and it's even rusty so I can give him lockjaw on top of whatever else. I wrap it in burlap and put it under my arm, and I go into the night and down the hill, and there are electric lights shining all around at the Navy Yard. You can even see the *Iowa* sitting there half lit up against the dark, and I guess maybe Miss Spencer's bluejacket is from the battleship, though he's too young to have been at Cuba. That was ten years ago, when I was still pretty much a baby, and this guy was probably knuckling little kids at his public school. Not for me, he wouldn't have. Not this guy. He's bad seed, as Pa likes to say.

There are three saloons on Front Street at the Navy end. I spend the next couple of hours drifting from one to the other and poking my head in now and then to check out the faces of the sailors, and then hanging around where I can, outside in the shadows, ducking the police when they come by, 'cause they'd take me as a boy-gone-bad. They'd nab me for loitering and street-roaming and for whatever they'd make of my weapon, though I'm ready to say my logger father needs it for work and I'm just trying to find him, the poor harmless drunk who's going off to the woods at dawn without his billhook. But I keep out of the way and nobody pays me any attention, and though the sailor I'm looking for isn't around yet, I'm ready to wait till he appears, and then till he's drunk and he can be taught a thing or two.

Finally, as I watch the sailors who got an early start at the saloon drifting out and back to their quarters, I realize they all have to go down Front and past the park. So I find a thicket of bushes at the street edge of the place and kind of burrow in where I can't be easily seen, but I can watch everyone going by. I wait and wait. And then I wake up with a start. I grab fast at my billhook and it's still there beside me. I look around. The street is quiet. It's very late. I come out of hiding and go down Front, and I look in at the three saloons and they're almost deserted. The guy I'm looking for isn't there, and I head on home. Ma and Pa are both still sleeping so deep that for a second I think maybe a crook snuck in while I was gone and killed them.

The next day I'm a perfect model of a schoolboy. I definitely don't want to be kept in, even for twenty minutes, 'cause when the final bell rings I go down the road and find the billhook all wrapped up by the tree where I left it, and I slide around out of sight and wait for Miss Spencer to go by. When she does, I step out and follow her. Today I'm going to stick right behind her all the time. I'll take my beating for missing dinner and the damn beer pail and bedtime and breakfast, even. Not to mention I'll take my hanging, if it comes to that. If this bluejacket starts beating on Miss Spencer, even if he's cold sober, I'll go at him right then and maybe that'd be just as well, with the cause real clear to everybody.

She's moving kind of slow. She doesn't really want to go to him. I don't blame her. If only I was somebody, I'd just go on up to her right now and say, Come with me instead, and we could do that, we'd just walk off together. But she leads me down toward town and I can see the bay out in front of us looking real blue and peaceful, and then Miss Spencer does something I don't expect. She takes a path off the road and heads up into the hills, up toward the old growth on the edge of town that the loggers haven't got to. The bluejacket and her are meeting somewhere secret this time. He thinks he won't have to worry about people seeing him if he gets upset with her and he can do what he wants. It's good I'm along. We're on barely a walking path now, through a shaggy meadow coming up on a big wall of trees as tall as a Seattle skyscraper. I don't want her to know I'm around, so I hang back quite a ways and she never looks behind her.

We go on into the dark of the woods and I have to stay closer to Miss Spencer with all the turns in the path. But there's more places to duck behind, as well, and I tread real light, like a redskin, staying on the mossy parts when I can. We play up here sometimes in the summer. We sneak around with rifles carved out of wood and we hunt the Suquamish and the Chimakum and the Muckleshoot, some of us being the Indians. When I'm Chief Seattle no one can ever find me till I plug them in the back, and I never have to give away nothing to the white man. There are real Indians out here, too, real off-the-reservation Indians, hop pickers mostly, farming and fishing between seasons. So we never know when we're going to run right into someone real, face to face.

I think about giving the bluejacket a few extra blows for making Miss Spencer come all this way alone. She's just turned out of sight ahead, beyond a tangle of dead trunks, and there's a strong smell of decaying wood in the air. I make the same turn she did around the dead trees, and ahead of me the path falls down a little slope to a clearing where there's a couple of shacks close by each other made of waste slabs from the sawmill and Miss Spencer is heading straight for them. Then a couple of Indians step out to meet her and I jump off to the side so they can't see me, but I flatten out on the ground and crawl under a thicket at the edge of the clearing and peek down on them.

The Indians are an old couple. The man, in raggedy overalls, is moving over to the second shack, which has cattails drying on the porch and woven hop baskets bunched up beside it. He goes in. The woman is wrapped in a blanket and her braids are hanging on her shoulders, and she's real old. Miss Spencer has turned this way and the two women are talking. Miss Spencer lays her hand on that place below her stomach where he hits her with his fist. She's crying. I can see that from this far away. Then the Indian woman puts her arm around Miss Spencer and takes Miss Spencer's hand in hers and they move off to the other shack, the old woman talking low and gentle all the time.

It's now I realize he's not coming. This has to do with how he's hurt her. I don't like the doctor in town either. He comes with his black bag and never says a word, and he looks over his glasses at me like it's my fault, even if I've got a broken rib. Maybe this Indian woman has some medicine that'll help Miss Spencer. And maybe her coming here alone means she's quits with him. I reach into the burlap and squeeze the handle of the billhook, and I think about catching this guy on Front Street tonight. I wonder if maybe I'll find out what my Pa is thinking when he does what he does to me. Of course, Pa's never actually gone and killed me. Or even hacked at me with a blade. But it's got to be pretty much the same. I'll lift my hand to the guy from behind and I'll strike at him over and over, and he'll crouch down, bleeding heavy already from the first strikes, and being too weak and drunk to put up a fight. He'll cry for mercy for a while and then he'll see it's no good and just shut up and take it. That's him. But what about me?

I sit and wait, trying to imagine. What if I was Pa. And then it seems real simple. I hate your guts, is all it is. I just hate your guts. I'm starting to cry. And then there's crying from inside the shack. A sharp shout and then some crying like Miss Spencer knows I'm here and she can feel what a kid feels and she knows. I'm ashamed of my own tears but they keep on coming. Say, don't I want to go help her, if she's hurting? But don't I realize that Indian woman is doing all she can, and she knows things I haven't even dreamed of? And say, aren't I crying myself like the child that I am? So I get up and drop that old billhook at my feet, and I go on along the path through the trees, and to hell with my Pa if he wants his old billhook ever again. To hell with him.

SILENCED VOICES:
WRITERS AND ANTI-TERROR

by Siobhan Dowd

The word *terrorist* is not new. British statesman Edmund Burke, writing of the French Revolution shortly before his death in 1797, wrote "Thousands of those Hell-hounds called Terrorists are let loose on the people." The word has had many manifestations since, referring to revolutionaries, secessionists, whistleblowers, freedom fighters, anarchists, religious zealots—the list goes on. The leaders of apartheid South Africa once insisted that Nelson Mandela was a terrorist. So far as the Israeli government was concerned, Yasser Arafat was a terrorist while he was rendered stateless, but when he became leader of the Palestinian Authority, the term was generally dropped—now, in the context of renewed hostilities, he is a terrorist once more. For many years, the United Nations has been debating a definition on the word; as time passes, the quest proves almost a holy grail. The standpoint of

Glimmer Train Stories, Issue 51, Summer 2004
©2004 Siobhan Dowd

the person using the term, the justification or otherwise of the motives that leads to the terrorist act, and whether or not that act is violent are all criteria on which clear agreement is elusive.

September 11, 2001 was a day the word *terrorism* took on yet more chameleon appearances. Suddenly on everybody's lips, it was a global threat over-riding national boundaries. The U.S.A. declared a "war on terrorism." This new kind of war would have many battlefields, both actual and metaphorical. Aside from the fighting on the ground in Afghanistan and Iraq, a raft of legislation was hastily introduced, nationally, regionally, and internationally. Many of the new "anti-terror" laws (notably the Patriot Act in the U.S.) aim to stop the terrorists before they carry out their deeds. As such, they must presume guilt by intent—a new concept, and one which rests uneasily with the rule of law, which assumes innocence until guilt is proven, and insists that an intent is a far cry from the crime. The example set by the world's most powerful country was promptly adopted by other nations eager to clamp down on local dissent. Al-Qaeda sprouted tentacles in unlikely places. A government had only to claim a nebulous al-Qaeda link with their local insurgents to silence criticism of what hitherto had been condemned as heavy-handed abuse.

International PEN, the writers association, recently analyzed its figures over the last five years for the number of writers and journalists imprisoned, prosecuted, attacked, or otherwise forcibly silenced in the course of carrying out their professional duty around the world. A resulting chart shows a steady rise after 9/11, with the numbers rising from roughly 600 to 800 in 1999 and 2000, to nearly 1200 in 2002. PEN has also published a report on the victims of this new anti-terrorism crusade. It reveals a real deterioration in conditions for writers in at least thirty-five countries. Its inescapable conclusion is that being a writer or journalist is more dangerous post-9/11 than it was pre-9/11. The reasons, it argues, are vague, over-broad anti-terror laws being applied to legitimate, non-violent dissent and local clamp-downs on separatism (such as in Chechnya, the Basque country, or in the Kurdish-populated southeast of Turkey) in the name of global security.

The PEN report also describes the passage of new anti-terror and national-security laws in such varied countries as South Africa, Mozambique, Morocco, El Salvador, Australia, India, and Indonesia. In addition it describes a global "anti-terror climate" whereby old laws, used infrequently before 9/11, are now invoked routinely. As the *Asia Times* put it in an opinion piece of January 10, "As the U.S.-led campaign against terrorism spreads, more and more governments in Asia and elsewhere are jumping on the bandwagon and cracking down on suspected terrorist groups. The trouble is that in the process, the definition of terrorism is continually getting widened to include everything from ethnic separatism and religious extremism to plain old-fashioned determined political opposition."

China, for example, has used 9/11 as a springboard for a new campaign to silence "independent elements" in Xinjiang, a predominantly Muslim region where a movement of ethnic Uighurs advocate full autonomy. The Foreign Ministry made claims that this movement colluded with "international terrorist forces," and strengthened its Strike Hard campaign in that province. Dozens of arrests and executions followed, many of which Amnesty International said were arbitrary. Tohti Tunyaz, for example, a writer and doctoral student, has been caught up in the repression. He serves an eleven-year term for allegedly inciting national disunity and attaining state secrets.

In Morocco, several journalists found themselves jailed under the new laws. Ali Lmbaret, for example, served several months of a three-year term for "insulting the person of the king," committing an "offense against the monarchy," and "an offense against territorial integrity." He was released on appeal only after he staged a life-threatening hunger strike, which was accompanied by a vociferous international campaign against his detention.

In Russia, the government was quick to claim links between al-Qaeda and Chechynyan rebels. The global anti-terror climate and the hostage-taking of civilians in a Moscow theatre by Chechnyan partisans led to new and fiercer measures being adopted to quash the uprising. These included repressive legislation aimed at muzzling the press. For the moment, sanity prevails: President Putin, after meeting with senior members of the press, has vetoed the proposed restrictions and the matter is still under debate. As the well-known Russian writer Anna Politkovskaya—an author who has faced prosecution for her own criticism of Russia's handling of Chechnyan affairs—argues, knee-jerk violence and the dismantling of civil liberties is ineffective at halting terrorism. Those measures only beget a downward spiral of violence and hate: "…the anti-terror machinery simply doesn't work," she writes. "Not one of the goals of the anti-terror operation has been realized. The terrorist leaders are still at large. And the resistance easily replenishes its ranks with new recruits seeking revenge for the suffering and deaths of family members."

Her words should serve as a caveat to all world leaders in these dangerous times. As Susan Sontag pleaded in a *New York Times* article on the first anniversary of 9/11, alternatives to "continuing to invoke the dangerous, lobotomizing notion of endless war" must be found if the world is to become truly safer.

Readers may like to contact their own governments about the complex issue of guarding against terrorist attacks while guarding with equal vigor the fundamental right to freedom of expression. In Britain and the United States, they would be:

Rt. Hon. David Blunkett M.P.
Home Secretary
House of Commons
London SW1A 0AA

The Honorable John Ashcroft
The Attorney General
U.S Department of Justice
950 Pennsylvania Avenue, NW
Washington, DC 20530

Siobhan Dowd of International PEN's Writers-in-Prison Committee in London writes this column regularly, alerting readers to the plight of writers around the world who deserve our awareness and our writing action.

The author on September 16, 1979.

Jenni Lapidus received a special mention in the 2002 Pushcart Prize and was nominated for the 2003 Pushcart Prize. She has published stories in *Hampton Shorts*, *Literal Latte*, and *Happy*, and was a finalist in *Glimmer Train Stories*' Very Short Fiction Contest. She is at work on her first novel.

HOT HOUSE

Jenni Lapidus (signature)

Jenni Lapidus

In the hot house, there were always two silver pitchers of coffee in the refrigerator. The windows were never open. The blinds were always down. There were no plants or pets. There was no music. I smoked cigarettes out my bathroom window after midnight, fourteen floors above Park Avenue. My parents had followed the rules and succeeded by them. Here it was, then. This was it. I used to sit on the toilet seat with my feet on the wall, writing, smoking, and waiting to leave. Funny, I lived in New York City, yet was convinced that nothing would happen to me until I went away. I still confuse the feeling of being safe with the feeling of being trapped.

On weekends, we slept like champions. My mother walked around in a green robe, my father and brother in their underwear. We watched television from our separate beds. The heat blew down—we could hear it—from the vents in the corners of our rooms. There was not enough air, but if it was difficult to breathe, it was easy to eat ice cream in the kitchen or lie in the mirrored gallery drinking Coke through a straw, to bathe so long my mother came pounding on the door.

"It would be nice to just be *in* there," says my brother, Bean, nodding at the ocean.

"Except it's so cold and dark." I take a sip of my drink. "And wet."

The night before, we'd ordered a "vacation package," a liter of rum and three cans of Coke, to our room. Now we're huddled on the blue rubber floor of our balcony on the Golden Princess. Our parents are in a suite across the hall.

"I *love* cruises," says Bean, handsome and slim, just out of his first semester of college. "I love cruises and I hate school."

"The first year of school is tough."

"I'm supposed to be having a good time," he says. "I'm supposed to be having a *grand* time."

"You have a broken heart."

He nods. "I know. The bitch."

I rub his knee. "I want to pull out your bad feelings," I say.

"Hippie."

I stand up.

"Oh, hippie, don't be mad. Hey, you're not going in to read, are you?"

I shake my head. I slide open the glass door to our room and light a cigarette, then step back out into the warm wind.

Bean is still staring at the water.

"I can't believe it, Kate," he says. "I'm weirder than you are."

"It's not a contest," I say.

"I know. But if it were a contest, I'd win."

"I'm not convinced."

"You'll believe me when I kill myself."

"Not funny, Bean."

"Not kidding, Kate."

"You'll go to hell."

"Jews don't believe in hell."

"Sometimes they do," I say. "Besides, you can't leave me. I can't be an only."

"You did fine for six years before me."

"Five and a half."

"You wanted a dog or a sister."

"I love you," I say. "Hey. You *can't*."

"In four months I'll be dead."

I don't say anything.

"Sorry, dude," Bean says. "April twenty-fourth. I'm outta here."

"Why April twenty-fourth?"

"I'm just letting you know."

We stand and face each other. He is younger, taller, and stronger than I am.

"Bean—you're not weirder."

"Am too."

"You had a serious relationship."

"I had a sick relationship," he says.

"You can drive."

He raises his eyebrows and turns away from me. I follow him inside. Bean turns on the television to the ship's channel, which is a twenty-four-hour view of the water in front of the ship. We'd laughed discovering this the first day: *How thrilling.* Now we leave it on while we fill out breakfast forms, conscious of our movement through the dark. The water divides, white then blue. We pull the thin blankets up to our chins.

"Promise me you won't hurt yourself tonight," I whisper.

"I promise I won't hurt myself, tonight."

Growing up, I locked myself out on a regular basis. The doormen kept a complete set of keys to the building, but my family only let them copy our bottom key, to make sure our neighbors couldn't break into our apartment. I sat in the hot hallway, reading Sexton or Plath, until my father found me. My father was in multiple litigations with the building. The men cordially abhorred him. The wives glowered at my mother in the elevator. She ignored them, a sad smile on her face, scooping keys from her pocketbook, pushing open the door to our apartment, hoping it would open onto a variation of her life. Or maybe that was me hoping.

"Go live in a teepee," Bean yelled, thirteen years old, dribbling a basketball from flower to painted flower across the white boards of my room.

"You go live in a teepee," I yelled back. He slammed the door, then opened it one squeaky inch. I was home from college for the weekend of Bean's bar mitzvah. Friday night, I'd taken a car home from the airport. Bags of pistachio nuts and sugar-free chocolates waited on my desk next to a stack of mail and a long list from my mother. I think my father was in bed. My mother and I sat on my bed and went over her list. When she left, I scurried to the kitchen and shoved a carton of Edensoy into the refrigerator. I lit incense in my room, like a belated teenager, and watched two hours of reruns on Channel 11. I fell asleep in my childhood bed that had been my mother's childhood bed.

"Go be a Buddhist," Bean said when I suggested he and I take an early walk through Central Park. His service was at Temple Emanu-El at ten.

"You go be a Buddhist," I said.

"I'm a Jew," he said. "I'm a man."

"All right, *man*."

There were five bathrooms in the hot house. In mine, with its peach wallpaper dotted with white clover, its peach and white tile floor, the Italian toilet and elegant sink, the mirrored cabinet framed in lightbulbs like a backstage dressing table, the white Formica hamper, tiny gray wastebasket, gray bathmat and matching towels, I felt every me I'd ever been.

After the service, my mother and I patted our blown-straight hair with our painted nails. We fidgeted with the gold hearts around our necks.

Bean laughed with the boys and danced with the girls. I got drunk and danced with my uncles. My father passed out in a bathroom stall.

"You goddamn writer," Bean said instead of goodbye as the doorman moved my bags into the car bound for La Guardia.

I bought a fashion magazine in the airport. I drank a virgin mary on the plane and cried all the way to Cleveland.

My three best girls picked me up from the airport. One of them was coming off an acid trip, and with my fake-straight hair she would not look at me, afraid I'd become someone else.

•   •   •

Bean has two approaches to the nightly dinner on the cruise. Either he stares straight ahead and saws through his steak, his eyes like dark windows, or else he entertains us with a jangling, manic monologue on any number of topics.

"Can I eat a kangaroo?" he asks. My dad shrugs. My mom smiles. She recently dropped thirty pounds on a shake diet, and looks a bit like Blythe Danner. Encouraged, Bean goes on. "Can I eat an elephant? A zebra? An owl?"

My mother works on her nightly double portion of Caesar salad, without dressing, croutons, or cheese. "A hummingbird? A woodpecker?" My father lifts his drink. I poke whatever white fish I ordered and finish my glass of wine. "A lion? A tiger? A giraffe? A cat? A rhinoceros? A pigeon? A pig?"

"You can eat a pig," my father says.

I am aware of the sea beneath us, so much darker than the night. They pull on me: the night sky, the deep sea, and my family. On and on my brother asks—what animals can he eat?—a desperate comedian and we his desperate audience.

What I never expected to do and what I did was, a year and a half out of college, I moved back. Or maybe I lie, maybe I always expected it. How could I make it out in the world without my mother? I wrote notes in different notebooks and lost the notebooks. I stared at burnt-out lightbulbs and wondered what to do about them. I'd lost three jobs in succession. I'd been sick all winter, something vague and bronchial. I threw up regularly from coughing. I stood frozen in my room—we'd moved to Brooklyn by then—and I couldn't unpack and I couldn't get out of bed. I was fucking a boy who told me not to fall in love with him, that he would not be falling in love with me, and I thought, *Fine*. I thought, *Good*. At least I didn't have to worry about him then, about him wanting to take me and keep me.

There were a lot of plants, my housemate's, and they trailed dirt onto the hardwood floor of my living room. The toilet didn't flush and the radiator wouldn't turn on. The refrigerator housed bags of turning produce, expiring milk, and compost in the bottom bin. My clothes piled up in the closet, dirty or clean, I didn't understand the difference. Water trickled from a hole in the ceiling into a pot I'd somehow managed to place there. I wore a hat to bed. I did not know what month it was. I could not locate the key to the mailbox. I could not locate the telephone. I was irritated with the girls, with their refusal to see that I was dying, consumed as they were with their million projects. I scowled at them from the couch, but if they noticed my looks they never let on. I could see what they could not see, that they were burning up the air in the house.

One night, the boy I was trying not to fall in love with looked across the table at me and said, "Sweet girl," and I think we both knew he saw through me. I followed him through the confusing streets of the West Village. We sat on the stairs in the weird blue light of his apartment building, breaking up, again.

"Don't leave and go out into the rain," he said. "Stay in here where it's warm. Let's not be all hands and tongues. I'm not telling you I won't fuck you, but I'm asking you. What do you want? What in the world do you *want* from me?"

I stared at the salad my housemate's boyfriend gave me. I accepted their wine. I smoked. Smoking was good. It opened up faraway places in my head and it hurt like I was smoking a hole right through my heart. I began spending more and more nights uptown. I followed the route with dream logic. I took the L under the river to Union Square. In the station, a man danced with a Styrofoam woman. Her feet were attached to his by string. They twirled too close and I smacked them with my purse. He lost his balance and fell toward me—crushing her fake body between us.

A second train, three stops, and I was at 86th and Lexington. I walked a block to Park Avenue. The cabs hurried uptown and downtown. Just to stand on the corner across from my building was to feel heat pressing against closed and covered windows.

The lobby was still my lobby, off-yellow walls, marble floor. I looked haggard in the ornate mirror by the side of the elevator, in the mirror in the elevator, and in the mirror next to our door. Having forgotten my key, I banged the gold knocker inscribed with our family name.

"Who is it?" my mother asked, out of breath.

"It's me," I said. "I'm sick."

Here, it was just right to be depressed. My mother was watching a high-school sitcom in the living room. My father put a pint of coffee ice cream upside down in the microwave for fifteen seconds. He dropped three scoops into a glass bowl and mashed it up like he used to, when I was small. He gave it to me and I nodded, thanks, and went back into the living room with my mother.

In the black-and-white kitchen, my mother went over Bean's college applications. Then she copied Bean a new list from her old list with a mechanical pencil. Behind her was the silver restaurant-size refrigerator with no magnets or fingerprints. Behind me was a row of silver cabinets. The first, the junk cabinet, was filled with plastic boxes of candy bars, level stacks of cookies, pretzels, crackers, and potato chips. The second cabinet held sardines and tuna fish, peas and corn and soups, arranged by type, four deep, neater than a supermarket. The third was rows of two-liter bottles and cans of Coke. Why had I ever run from this perfection? I tucked my legs underneath me on the black rubber chair. In this land of heat and no decisions, I sat drinking coffee with my mother in my mother's kitchen. Between us sat a bowl of fake croissants. The refrigerator hummed its song, *Don't go, don't go.* My mother said, "I swear I do not care what you do. But you are please going to have to do something." I'd scared her by sitting in her kitchen all day long and enjoying it. I told her this was really all I wanted to do, sit with her in her perfect kitchen.

I took a long shower and got myself off. Then I sat down on the floor of the tub holding the detachable shower over my head. The water ran down my face. The beads of water on the shower door were very beautiful.

It looked like I had taken it all too seriously. Bean was a model high-school senior, captain of two teams, winner of the scholar-athlete award. He'd been accepted early-action into the Ivy League. My parents and I stayed out of his way. He ordered sandwiches on the telephone. He closed the door and got into bed with his girlfriend. Or else he occupied the kitchen with his teammates, boys who were large and loud in the house. His girlfriend was sexy and relaxed, easy around my parents. She stood in the doorway to my room, with long hair and large breasts, drinking a Diet Coke. She asked, "How's it going?"

"Going," I told her, "it is not." I swallowed the laugh in my throat.

Uptown is where I went to feel the old feeling of being in trouble. I knew I was in trouble in Brooklyn, but it went unacknowledged. The girls never yelled, never slammed doors and berated me. They offered miso soup and wine. I went uptown to be a failure in peace.

My mother said, "Please apply to graduate school. Oh! Please apply to graduate school," and so I pretended to apply. One of the side effects of pretending to apply to graduate school was that, in May, I got accepted to graduate school. By that time, the boy had left the city. I did not want to be a student. I got a job and moved back to Brooklyn.

But before any of that happened I spent months acting out a demented play with my mother, with whom I was desperately in love. I sat on the beanbag chair in the corner of my room and watched her fold my clothing. I followed her to the grocery store, humming at her heels. In the morning she cooked me cream of wheat. In the afternoon she brought me sushi. I sat in the kitchen, writing an essay on why I wanted an MA, while a woman mopped the floor and a second woman clipped my mother's toenails.

Bean meets me at my office. I switch off the lights and lock the door.

"There are so many good reasons to be dead," he tells me, instead of hello.

I don't know what to say to him. He looks bad, but attractive: too thin, his blue eyes bright from too many thoughts and not enough sleep. He'd called that morning, full of questions about Dad and hell, and I'd told him, "Bean, I'm at work. I can't have this conversation at work. Please. Get on a train and come see me."

We walk twelve blocks to 10th and A. It's a clean, cold February night but Bean insists he's warm enough in just his long-sleeved shirt.

He says he doesn't care where we go, he doesn't eat anymore, so I pick a good Italian restaurant with clocks on the walls. I order a carafe of house wine and two plates of pasta.

"I saw my future, Kate, a man trapped inside a man, in a suit inherited from Dad. I can't eat. I can't sleep. I'm failing psychology. I keep walking out of class. I can't bear to listen to the professor explain every single thing that's wrong with me! I have castration anxiety, Kate. I've got an Oedipus complex, big time."

"You're having a hard time," I say, filling his glass.

"I'm already gone," he tells me. "You know, I've always been gone."

"What are you talking about?"

"I've been going through my photos. I'm not really here. I've never really been anywhere. I'm superimposed. Not everyone's meant to do great things, Kate. Some people aren't meant to live."

"Eat a little," I say. "It's tasty."

He shakes his head.

"Life is long," I tell him. "Look at me. I'm doing good now, right?"

"I'm so glad. You'll be okay without me."

"No," I tell him and I start to cry. "No. I'm not doing that well, just better."

"A lot better," he says. "Remember when the telephone made you cry every time it rang? And I was so mean about it? I didn't understand, but now I understand. I understand perfectly."

This makes me smile, but my eyes and nose are still running. He's referring to the wake-up calls during our trip to Hong Kong the year before, twelve days during the time I lived at home, twelve days that didn't touch me, that, except for the fright of the plane taking off, and the heartbreaking ring of the phone, I can't remember.

We ride to Brooklyn together. I buy cookies we don't eat and rent a movie we don't watch. I put him to bed on the couch, but in the morning he's in bed with me. I make him shower. We travel into Manhattan together and then we split. I go to work and he goes to Penn Station to catch a train back to school. It's a busy day and when

Bean calls to let me know he's made it back, I realize I haven't been thinking about him.

At night, my mother and I watched her shows. During the commercials, I shook and repeated, "I've ruined my life."

"What have I done?" she wailed as I stood, hysterical, in her doorway, unable to figure out what to wear outside. It was impossible to feel the weather inside our house, where there was only one kind of weather, hot, and it didn't occur to either of us to crack the window and feel the air outside. She lifted a blind and said, "People are wearing jackets but not hats."

I shrieked and crumpled to the floor.

"Oh my god," she said. "My god, I've created a little monster."

Despite therapy and meds, Bean is getting worse. He leaves me telephone messages at hours when no one should be awake. He claims to be so thin his cheekbones jut out of his face. He says he wants to die and is afraid to die. He says he loves me and is so sorry that he is going to die.

I visit him. I think he looks all right, but I have a thing for skinny boys and boys who are losing their minds.

We lie in the park. It is March and warm in the sun. He says, "I don't know how to clean my room."

"I know about that," I say.

"I have no idea how to look after myself. I love Mom," he says. "It's sick. I need Mom. It's going to be me and Mom forever."

I stay the afternoon. He shows me his dorm, the student union, the library. He stands with me while my train arrives.

"Bean," I say, hugging him. "I thought it was over for me, too. But life is long."

"But I'm so much more fucked up than you!" he cries, as I get on the train and leave him, and in the weeks that follow he proves it, with his relentless talk of hell, muscles decaying, sex-change operations, his room growing light and dark at the edges.

•   •   •

After I put my hands around my mother's throat, she threw me to the floor in the little yellow room where various women had lived as our maids, and ordered me to stay out of her way. "I feel like you want to eat me!" she said.

It was true. I wanted to consume my mother. I loved her fiercely and hated her for the game we played. I would have climbed in the bath with her if she'd have let me. I wanted to sleep in the bed with my mother, but my father was in the way. I hopped up and down in my room in a nightshirt. I laughed. When I got outside it a little and saw myself hiding in the hot house, hopping, scaring my mother, I laughed and laughed.

"Why are you laughing?" my mother demanded, her eyes full of real terror.

"Because it's so fucking funny!" I screamed, giggling, tears leaking down my face.

My father ignored me.

Bean asked, "Have you really gone crazy? Really really crazy?"

I dreamt I lived in a corduroy house full of lost people, old and sick. I called my mother on the telephone. "What am I doing here?"

"It's a good place to rest."

"No, it's ugly and upsetting. Come and get me."

I looked at the list with all the patients' names typed on it. Next to some of the names it said *voluntary* and next to others it said *committed*. It took me a while to find my name. When I found it, I saw that next to my name it said, *to the grave.*

I made an appointment with the therapist. I cancelled. I rescheduled. I cancelled. It hurt to go crazy all alone and simultaneously; I worried it was merely my fantasy to go crazy. It was my deepest fear and my deepest wish.

My parents bring Bean back to the city and wait with him in the emergency room and check him, at his insistence, into the psychiatric ward at New York Presbyterian. I am afraid to go to him, that first night. I go cook dinner for my boyfriend instead. I have these things now—a job, a boyfriend—and I'm scared the madness is contagious.

What if my mother, father, brother, and I can never get free of each other?

Nevertheless, the next day after work I bribe myself with a cookie and go up to the hospital.

I get off the bus going down 68th and throw up. Peanut butter in the cookie. I throw up again a block from the hospital. The itching in my throat increases. I show my ID to security, walk through the recycled air of the lobby, and ride the elevator up to the top floor. I find the ward with its list of forbidden items—razors, coat hangers, cigarettes, plastic bags, pencils and pens. I ring the bell. A nurse brings me in and leads me to a closed room. My family and Bean's ex-girlfriend sit at a low table with a doctor.

"Hi, Bean," I say.

He stands up, like a host, to hug me. "Are you okay, Kate?"

"I'm having an allergic reaction," I tell the group.

"I'm not sure how to deal with that," says the doctor. He walks me out of the room and passes me to a different doctor. "I think she's having an anaphylactic reaction." This doctor rides me down to the emergency room and leaves me with the broken bodies. Has it happened again? Have I crossed the line that separates the well from the sick? Overcome with the need to shit, I run to the lockless bathroom.

Several strangers walk in on me.

"Sweetie?" my mother asks, opening the door a crack.

"Christ," I say. "Come on in. How's Bean?"

She closes the door behind her. I grin up at her from the toilet.

"They say he's got a personality disorder. They're putting him in blue group. Blue for mood disorder. The yellow group is for patients with psychotic disorders. So it's good he's in blue, right? He'll be okay. They have a lot of activities. They even have lectures and yoga. Maybe it will be like camp."

"I'm feeling a lot better," I say. I pull up my pants. "I'm ready to go up and see him."

"His visiting hours are over," my mom says, gently.

I am the last to arrive at my grandparents' apartment in Midtown for the first night of Passover.

My mother opens the door and purses her lips at me. "Did you get my message?"

I had. Her message said not to wear jeans.

"Did you get my message and think, *Fuck you*?"

"No," I say. "These are the nicest pants I own."

We drink champagne and eat gefilte fish with horseradish and celery filled with low-fat cream cheese. If my brother were here, we'd be poking each other on the couch.

We take our places at the traditional Seder table my grandmother has set. She hands out the prayer books, the covers of which are wrapped in tinfoil. "The covers were so dirty," she explains.

My mother reads the passages on peace sarcastically.

My grandmother slices the flourless cake so thin it falls apart.

Since I'm the only kid, I'm the only one looking for the afi-komen. I hit the usual spots, behind the *New Yorkers* and *Vanity Fairs*, between the door and wall of the guest bedroom, under the pillows on the couch. The chatter is loud from the dining room. If my brother were here we'd be tripping all over each other trying to win. I check underneath the couch, though I can't imagine my grandfather would bend down to put it there.

I go into the dining room. My grandmother is saying, "They can take everything, every last thing, as long as they leave me my laundry machine."

"I can't find it," I mumble.

"Do you want a hint?" asks my grandfather.

I shake my head. He stands and I follow him into the guest bedroom. He lifts up the life-size leather schnauzer. "Not even a tricky spot."

My brother and I sit together on attached chairs looking out at the lights of the city. He opens the bag of apples I've brought him from the farmer's market. He takes an apple in each hand. He says, "Growing up, I felt like everyone in the building hated us."

"Everyone did hate us," I say.

"Right," he says. "Right." He takes two bites, one out of each apple. Then he laughs, and I laugh, too. It is eight o'clock on a Friday night in April. That it is eight means visiting hours are over in an hour. That it is Friday means he's been here two weeks. That it is April means he's not on spring break in Florida with the college friends he says he doesn't have.

"Let's take a lap," suggests Bean.

We stroll around the lounge.

"I like it here," he says.

I do not like it here. It is overheated and smells like plastic and apple juice. There is a ping-pong table and an understocked bookshelf and seven or eight dirty board games. There is not enough air and I am locked in. To leave I have to go and ask someone to let me out.

I walk the blocks away from the river with small steps and keep my back straight. I do not think about my parents. I do not worry about my brother or the long night ahead of him. I walk in a line toward the subway. I will go home and shower and put on mascara, then out to meet my boyfriend for a sandwich and a beer in the bar on my corner, like a *normal girl*.

The doctors take Bean out of his single and move him in with an old man who tells my brother he ought to be "out chasing girls," and a guy in his late twenties who sits in the lotus position on his bed reading math books. Bean gets a day pass. We sit by the boat pond in Central Park.

"This is Stuart Little's pond," he says.

"I know," I say.

We eat lunch in a diner. He eats and eats and finally says, "On the medication, I can't feel when I'm full."

Bean moves home with my parents halfway through April. He has put on weight, takes two medications, and crosses the park for therapy three times a week. He's agreed to give school another go in the fall. In the meantime, he applies for summer classes at Columbia and a drawing class at the Y. We have plans to make tacos together next week at my house. We have tickets to a Broadway show in June. We have plans to travel to Australia before I'm thirty. This weekend he's out in the Hamptons with my parents.

When my mother calls to tell me, I'm in my living room watering plants. It's eight in the morning and the sun is beginning to show. A jogger found Bean, she says. Her voice is high and slow—I understand now why people ask you to sit down for certain news—as she tells me that my brother took a variety of pills with half a bottle of vodka. A jogger found Bean, drowned on the beach. *She hadn't heard him awake in the house. She hadn't heard him leave the house. She hadn't heard him stumble down the steps under her window.* I put my hand through our glass coffee table.

The next afternoon, drunk and not at work, I get a photograph from Bean in the mail. Behind my brother the back of a white truck is framed by part of a building and a cluster of blurred red and blue lights. The street looks shiny, as if with recent rain. I've just stepped off the curb into Bean's shadow. Over my left shoulder, an Asian man looks down the street and the shapes of two people lean against the exit of a subway station. The picture cuts off an inch below our shoulders. I am wearing something gray and shapeless and a gray scarf. There is a pimple on my chin. My mouth is tight and turned down. My left cheekbone, too, looks tight. My eyes are concealed by large sunglasses. Two bobby pins pull the curls of my awkward haircut away from my face. My forehead is lifted slightly in question.

My brother wears a navy sports jacket that slopes elegantly toward his neck. The top button on his shirt is undone. His neck is angled toward the photographer, our father. His lips are neutral. His eyelids are low over the tops of his blue irises. The skin underneath his eyes is red then blue. If Bean looks any one thing, it's disappointed. The back of the picture is dated in my mother's precise handwriting, December 31, 2000. This was the week the telephone made me cry every time it rang. This was after Bean had been accepted into college and over a year before he started to break down. We look cut and pasted against the muted background, which is how we felt, certainly, those two weeks in Hong Kong, with our family, and also how we felt a great deal of the time.

In the half-inch between our shoulders part of a woman in an orange sweatshirt bends under a slice of pale street. In the large space between our faces and above us are a piece of bridge and a rectangle of flat white air. Bean included a card with his full name and the date, April 24, 2002, at the top, and the words: *We look like movie stars. Sad ones.*

I'd like to say that the last time I saw Bean was in the park, that we were active and delighted in the open air, but it was underground, in a subway station. I watched him walk away, then ran to make my own train.

As the train sped through its tunnel, I was hot and among strangers. I had my hands at my sides, knees bent slightly for balance. I'd like to say I missed him then, my little brother, but as the train jolted to a stop, I was concentrating on keeping my equilibrium. I was not able to save him. What can any of us do for the breaking-up and breaking-down but witness them and wait it out—even when the broken ones are us? I was able to wait myself out and I had all the patience in the world for Bean to wait himself out, but Bean did not wait. It felt disgusting to think that I would eventually feel better—it feels dead to limit my regret.

SHORT STORY AWARD
FOR NEW WRITERS

1ST PLACE

Jennifer Tseng receives $1200 for "The Words *Honey* and *Moon*."

Tseng's bio is on page 68, preceding her story.

2ND PLACE

Xiaofei Chen receives $500 for "Burying Twelve Yuan,"
and publication in *Glimmer Train Stories*.

*Red cushions on the benches, fat red cushions like big sausages woven with flowers
and peacocks, are my offerings of comfort to the customer.*

Xiaofei Chen is a sophomore at Monte Vista Christian High in California. Her
time is split between friends, homework, piano, reading/writing, and, just
recently, learning to drive. She lives with her parents, sister, and dog, and wishes
to live to a ripe old age.

3RD PLACE

Katya Vondermuhll receives $300 for "Serenades."

*Father will always remain joyful, as we come and go, marry and divorce, have
children, divorce again, kick the front door open with our heels and say, Christ, but
not in the way we were taught.*

Katya Vondermuhll studied writing and Russian literature at Sarah Lawrence
College, where she received her BA. She lives in Boulder City, Nevada, with her
husband and newborn son, and is currently at work on a novel.

---

*We invite you to visit **www.glimmertrain.com** to see a list of the top twenty-five winners
and finalists. We thank all entrants for sending in their work.*

My father was drawn to zoos, perhaps because he was at ease in them, or perhaps because he thought they were suitable for children. In any case, we spent much of our leisure time in zoos, having our pictures taken next to the largest and/or most dangerous animals.

Jennifer Tseng received her MA in Asian-American Studies from UCLA, her MFA from University of Houston, and was twice a fellow at the Fine Arts Work Center in Provincetown, Massachusetts. Her work has appeared in *Green Mountains Review*, *Indiana Review*, and *Ploughshares*, and is forthcoming in *Grand Street*. "The Words *Honey* and *Moon*" is an excerpt from *Woo*, her novel-in-progress.

THE WORDS *HONEY* AND *MOON*

Jennifer Tseng

Woo honked the horn lightly, unconvinced by his wife's urgings that it was an American custom. He was as embarrassed by it as he was by the eight tin cans she had tied to the fender with string. Camille laughed at his timorous tapping and jokingly called it a "Chinese honk." Finally, when it was clear that he would not soon Americanize its duration or intensity, Camille leaned over, put both her trinketed hands on the car's black apple, and pushed with all her willowy might. The street filled with the music of their German car's horn and someone nearby honked back, though by this time they were miles away from the church. The few who had stayed on the front steps to wave and to whistle their support were out of earshot and the newlyweds were on their way west.

They drove, according to Woo's plan, directly from the church to Kenosha, Wisconsin, and arrived in plenty of time to visit the Kenosha County Zoo, first on their list of dazzling destinations. The Kenosha County Zoo was no petting zoo. It was the largest zoo in the state of Wisconsin and contained an endless array of exotic animals from all parts of the globe. There were, among other mammalian and ornithological treasures, black bears and Sika deer, a pair of giraffes from the African veldt, a snow leopard from the mountains of Central Asia, a Kivu Highlands gorilla, a flock of Palmetto flamingos, an Arabian cheetah cub (though no adult cheetahs), three black Louisianan swans, a few new-world monkeys, and a small family of zebras on loan from William Randolph Hearst's California ranch.

This multifarious collection met with Camille's instant approval and garnered for Woo a generous supply of bonus points in their slit-eyes-versus-green-eyes game. Her only grievance was that they did not have even one giant panda, the animal she most closely associated with China, and therefore with Woo. Husband-like, Woo quickly appeased her with an optimistic allusion to an upcoming (petting) zoo in Nebraska. In his eagerness to please her, he too became excited, and could almost see the dressy, oversized bears in his mind's eye, munching on crisp branches of young bamboo, next to their horse and cow neighbors.

For dinner they ate in a pleasant lakefront restaurant whose only distinguishing feature seemed to be its inclusion of a separate menu for children twelve and under, no doubt the feature that had captivated his colleague Mac's darling Isabelle, and earned the restaurant its place on their list. To Woo's delight, Camille confessed she had never tasted shellfish or steak. In the spirit of education, he recklessly ordered one of each for her, along with a prime rib for himself. She was more easily charmed by the shrimp, those C-shaped curls of coral flesh, than she was by the steak, which she greeted with confusion as a bloody, cabbage-less version of her mother's corned beef. Where were the peppercorns, she wanted to know. Didn't he agree that peppercorns and beef were perfect complements?

"Ah ha, you are so gourmet for someone who never try gourmet before," he teased.

"I am?" she asked, and her eyes went greener and rounder than he had ever seen them.

Woo found dinner on the whole banal. He took solemn note of the frozen vegetables and canned fruits and thought wistfully of the day he would pick fresh corn and carrots from his own backyard, plump oranges from his own Valencia tree. He declined dessert, but watched Camille suck on a series of spoonfuls of "orange" sherbet. The carnival color chilled him as much as the temperature of those soft sugary moons. He accepted a spoonful fed to him by her gemmed, ecstatic hand. But this he did only to surprise her, with the hope that she might open her eyes in response, which she did. The taste to his palate was cloyingly sweet and artificial. He patiently kept this knowledge to himself, the way a parent might suppress the falsehood of Santa Claus for the sake of a child, though he made plans to introduce her to something finer as soon as the opportunity presented itself. Belgian chocolate, he thought, or macaroons. Surely there would be no mung-bean pastries or shaved ice with coconut milk en route to the western coast of the United States, and so he called to his mind a list of all the superior European and American sweets he had tasted since his arrival in his wife's country.

"I'm still hungry," Camille said excitedly.

"That can't be," Woo laughed, while simultaneously calculating the bill so far. "Two appetizer, two entree, one dessert! Holy Toledo!"

"It's true," she smiled. "I get really hungry when I'm happy. Does that happen to you?"

"No such a thing. I'm hungry when I don't have food. Work hard, eat more. Exercise, eat more. Happy, no happy, this is irrelevant."

"Well I'm still hungry."

"Then you must be very happy," he said, looking at her directly.

"Mmmmhmmm," she hummed, her fingernail tapping the various dessert options in a jaunty dance on the laminated menu. "What do you think? A slice of apple pie with cheddar cheese, or raspberry cheesecake?"

Woo brooded silently for a moment over Americans' preoccupation with cheese. It was his own pet theory that cheese was the culprit responsible for America's obesity problem. He entertained the thought of his leggy, green-eyed child bride turned happy and voluptuous. He could get used to there being more of her, but if it meant eating out more often, whether or not his wallet could adjust was another story. Then he felt a pang of confusion. Had she ordered so much food because she was happy, or was she happy because she had ordered so much?

"Tell me which one to get," she said. "You choose and we'll share."

"No, no, no. I don't want. Your favorite you pick."

"Are you sure? Is it okay? Am I eating too much?"

"My poor growing girl," he said. "You eat! You eat!"

She ordered the cheesecake with a scoop of sherbet.

"Mother says I don't eat enough. But at home I'm never that hungry. It's not that I'm unhappy, just not happy enough to eat. Not like now with you. I'm so happy. Why do you think that is?"

Camille chattered away while Woo listened and interjected the occasional peppercorn of wisdom, just to please her conversational palate.

"In China we have a saying, the best appetizer is hunger. Eating is like getting married. When you wait, when you are patient, it tastes good. When you are hungry, everything tastes like the best."

Later, when the waiter came to bring their dessert, he found the table was so cluttered by the many dishes Camille had sampled that there was no place to slip the bill except next to her right elbow. Woo reached awkwardly over the dirty plates to take the ticket.

It dawned on him that she did not have any money, probably not even a few coins in her small beaded purse. What sort of girlish things did she store in there? Lipsticks and tissues, perfumes and picture postcards of places she had never been? Now and in the future he must pay for her. He pulled two blue twenty-dollar travelers' checks from his wallet and signed them carefully. A Chicago bank had issued them to him; he knew they were valid, but the blue, almost purple color of the notes was so different than the green of American currency. It looked to him more like play money, extracted from a children's game.

The Milky Way Motel was situated like a mole on Kenosha's high eastern cheekbone. Contrary to its illuminated sign, which promised a buxom braided blonde girl pouring a pitcher of glowing, milk-colored stars into the night sky, its small lobby contained a gaunt, spidery man with bruised eyes seated at a metal desk. Woo surmised that the girl from the billboard sign must have been born of this man's imagination, a girl from the world that existed behind the lids of his bruised eyes while he slept. It was dusk and the man looked as if he might doze off momentarily. He was wearing square, plastic reading glasses that magnified the shadows on his face as he scanned the classified section of a newspaper and sipped from a small tumbler of milk. There was a poster of the solar system on the wall behind him and a Swiss-cheese block paperweight on the desk. The green glass lamp by which he read was the only light in the room other than the moon. Had either newlywed known of such a thing, they might have thought the office looked like that of a California fortune teller's.

When Woo stepped into the dim, milk-scented lobby, the man held up a room key and continued scanning the classifieds.

"Good evening," Woo said, stepping up to the desk. "Pardon me, please. I am Joseph Woo. I have tonight reservations. Two people. Husband and wife."

The man continued reading and took a sip of milk. Woo wondered if he was to reach out and take the key from the man's hand. He didn't think it a wise idea.

"You're supposed to take the key," Camille whispered in his ear. "He's busy."

Something was wrong, Woo thought. He was sure this was not the custom. The man was supposed to take their names, signatures, identity verification. What kind of establishment was this?

He pulled out his wallet and found the three-by-three card that he had cut from a three-by-five to fit. There in his own Royal typescript were the words:

> The Milky Way Motel
> 725 Lake Dr.
> Kenosha, WI 53141

There were no Motel 6s in Wisconsin. Woo had hesitated each time he had booked a non-Six reservation. It was likely that independent motel keepers were not regulated to the extent that chain-motel keepers were. There was no systematic quality control, no centralized power to enforce high standards. The man at the Milky Way Motel was precisely the type Woo had feared: a lazy, unregulated clerk with no consideration for the customer.

He longed to be in Iowa—their next destination—where a Motel 6 clerk named Candy had not only given him clear directions to the motel but to the state fair as well. She'd recommended the apple fritters and had told him to have a safe trip.

He thought that if they stood in front of the reading man long enough, he would have to look up, that shame or self-consciousness or both would force him, but the man continued reading and sipping like a machine. In fact, he seemed so undisturbed that had he not been holding out the key, Woo would have thought he hadn't noticed them. Had he not been reading, Woo might have thought he was blind. Finally the man finished his milk. As he tilted his head back toward the solar system to allow the last drops to fall on his tongue, Woo snatched the key angrily out of his hand. Woo was defeated. His fantasy of driving through the night to Iowa had been brief. Their day had seemed as long as his stay in America, a small lifetime. His new wife was tired and he noted with affection that her green eyes were sleepy, verging on accidental slits. Such pale skin, such thin arms, such a long and fragile neck. So tired. They could not go back and they could not proceed. They must stay.

Woo carried both the suitcases upstairs to their room. Camille followed him like a sleepwalker. He fumbled with the key in the dark (surely Motel 6 would have lights burning near the doors at night), checked once more to see that it was room number eight, and then opened the door. The sight of the double bed filled his startled, exhausted body with an electrical current.

"Woo Tai Tai," he said brightly, trying to maintain his composure. "Welcome to your bridal room."

"Mister Woo," she said, climbing into the bed. "Your wife is very happy."

Woo turned the bedside lamp on and switched off the overhead light. Perhaps she would fall asleep immediately and he would not be faced with the frightening prospect of seducing her. He could not decide how to weigh his warring impulses. Which was heavier? His desire to touch her or his desire to avoid touching her? He didn't know. She seemed to have fallen deeply, prophetically asleep.

He leaned his face close to hers the way he had seen her do with the names of the smallest towns on the maps. Her orange blonde hair smelled of green apples and of the German wood of his father's roll-top desk. He had thought it would smell of persimmons. This is not to say he was disappointed, no, not even mildly. He was fond of the unexpected fragrance, but it was yet another indicator of his inability to calculate and predict in matters of Camille and/or in matters of the body. He continued to look at her face without touching it. He tried to understand its many parts, which moved even in sleep. The happy slits of her eyes quivered as she slept, and he could see the strange marbles of her eyeballs beneath the lids crossing back and forth as if reading a hidden book.

There was a light dusting of freckles on either side of her elfin nose, so few in each sprinkle that the marks seemed like a mistake or an afterthought on the part of her maker. Between her nose and her lips was a slight valley dotted with fine downy hair, so pale in color that it was visible to him now for the first time. Her lower lip was larger than the upper; it looked almost swollen, and he wondered if she was feverish. But her face was not flushed and he could feel without touching it that its temperature was cooler than that of his own. Her ears, which also surprised him by not detecting his approach, had lobes which were attached to the side of her face, so that the outline of the ear was one long continuous curve, unlike his own, whose curves were interrupted by the separation of the lobe from the rest of the ear. He thought hers a less formed and simplified version of his own. His discovery of this recessive trait pleased him in some way and emboldened him to touch her.

Of all her many girlish and alien traits, he found her eyebrows to be the most exquisite. Made of the same persimmon color as her hair, the brows were orderly, as if their maker had measured and cut and counted each feathery piece by hand, assembled the arcs, and then trimmed and combed them with a mechanical device. Woo touched each brow once with the tip of his middle finger as if painting them on. *Ruan de*, he thought. How soft. Softer than he could have predicted. Their softness made him all the more curious about the down valley above her lips. The fine pale hairs must be softer there in that ethereal slope, that tiny shadow. He thought to drag his tongue across the delicious ditch, but then Camille sighed heavily as if to warn him away. Better to let her sleep.

He took off his shoes and began to pad around the carpeted room in his socks. Through the picture window, he could see the dark shine of Lake Michigan. There were several boats in the dock and each one had a small light at its helm. The sight of the boats waiting to sail, the black water, filled him with sad thoughts, and so he walked away from the window and set to unpacking their things.

He would leave the curtains open so that his wife might see the water when she woke up. All through dinner she had looked at it and pleaded with him to take her to the beach the next day. She wanted to see everything in daylight. She wanted to lie on the sand. Was it like the ocean? She'd wanted to know. Though he'd planned to take her to a penny arcade, he deferred to please her and to defray costs.

He opened his wife's suitcase without thinking for a moment that she might see it as an invasion of privacy. He had nothing to hide. Why should she? He hung up her dresses and brought her yellow and white toiletry bag to the bathroom. He unzipped the bag and began rooting through its contents for her toothbrush, which he thought ought to be allowed to air dry, to protect it and the bag from mildew. Camille had the good habit of brushing her teeth after meals, but he guessed correctly that she seldom remembered to shake the brush after rinsing, and when she did, it was not with much vigor. Of course he had never witnessed her in the act of brushing, but she had shared her habits with him in the course of their many chats.

He found her white plastic brush and its wet bristles without difficulty, though not before leafing past several other items including a tube of lipstick, two paper packages each marked "slender regular tampon," a pair of tweezers, a beige compact, and a box of prophylactics still wrapped in cellophane, all of which electrified him, though it was the sinister cellophaned box that delivered the deepest bolt to his body's core. This was very bold of her. She had been thinking something about him. The most maddening current of fear and electricity crept through his fingers as he studied the box. It contained twelve prophylactics and among the many words printed on its modest back were "pleasure," "contact," and "sexual intercourse." Woo threw the box back in the bag, zipped the bag, and pulled his hands away in haste, as if the box or the bag might electrocute him.

He stepped back into the bedroom carefully, afraid now more than ever to wake her. He hung his own clothes up next to hers, pulled out a few more necessary items (a fresh bar of Dove soap, a wash cloth, a jar of peanuts, an orange, a Chinese-English dictionary, the latest issue of *Reader's Digest*, and a pair of gray pajamas), and then stowed the suitcases in the closet. Then, as quietly as he could, he arranged the peanuts, reading materials, and orange on his night stand and sat on the side of the bed furthest from Camille. Perhaps he should double check the lock on the door, he thought. This he did swiftly. And the window. Was there one in the bathroom? He couldn't remember. He brought his personal belongings into the bathroom and closed the door. Locked it. Leaned into the shower to look for a window and found nothing but a minty expanse of tile.

Woo ran the faucet until the water was hot, and then began turning the bar of soap over and over in his hands in order to produce a generous lather. He carried a bar of Dove with him wherever he went— to the University, to the library, to the movie house. Whenever he felt anxious, he excused himself from the situation and went to the nearest restroom to wash his face. The strong smell of the soap calmed him and the emollients left his skin feeling clean and elastic. Now he massaged the bubbles into his cheeks, breathed deeply, and waited for the familiar sensation to relieve him. What was wrong with him? The Dove trick had failed. He checked the bathroom lock and then changed into his gray pajamas. The light cotton trousers which were usually so comfortable made him feel exposed. The fabric was quite thin, almost sheer! Could she possibly see through it? No such thing. Ridiculous. Time for bed. You'll feel more relaxed tomorrow if you sleep.

Woo slipped into the bedroom. He turned off the bed lamp and climbed as stealthily as he could into the bed. He closed his eyes and tried to quiet his breathing. The sheets were cold and slick, though his bride's body emanated warmth from its brief distance. When he opened his eyes the room was filled with light and he was overcome by dread, thinking that morning had come. But only two minutes had passed. A large boat was docking, its lights flooding their room. He closed his eyes, and when it was dark again, he opened them.

Without moving his body, he turned his head to look at Camille. Her head was turned away from him, her hair a silky, messy flame on the white pillow. Slowly, slowly he lifted the covers up so that he might look at her. It was then that he was reminded she had climbed into bed fully clothed. This fact relaxed him somewhat, for now he was comfortably occupied with how wrinkled her clothes were becoming. Without a hint of irony, he said to himself that he should remove her clothing immediately and hang it up at once. There was the removal of clothing for the purpose of hanging it up, and there was the removal of clothing for other purposes. Each form of clothing removal was, in Woo's mind, easily compartmentalized, neither threatening to undermine the other, until, however, he reached out to unbutton the top button of his wife's blouse. He paused and boldly pulled the covers down to the foot of the bed so that he might see everything, only then beginning to understand his own truest motives.

To his utter fright and delight there were only four buttons on this particular blouse, so that once he had unbuttoned two, he was already halfway to dread or ecstasy, he didn't know which. He unbuttoned the third and fourth quickly, afraid again of waking her, and then realized that the real terror would be in pulling the blouse open to expose her. This he did, and almost choked on the air that was racing to

78   *Glimmer Train Stories*

reach his lungs. By a much-needed brand of newlywed's luck, he transformed the beginning of the choke into a subtle, even elegant throat clearing. He was determined not to wake her—not for fear that she would unwrap her sinister cellophane box, for that was swiftly seeming less and less sinister, but for fear that he might not complete his heavenly task of saving her wardrobe from wrinkles.

The skirt went next, side zipper, hook, eye, and then her red leather sandals with their crossed straps each fastened by a single sharp tooth of steel and a red tongue of leather, easy to release. As he arranged her sandals next to his own black shoes, his restless child bride pedaled her bare feet twice as if on a dream-manufactured bicycle, and made a gurgling little dove noise. Was she cold, he suddenly wondered? To him the room seemed warm—it was summer after all—but he could not presume to know how she felt then. Should he leave her underclothes intact and cover her? The wrinkles, unfortunately, were no longer an issue. He scanned the room for a thermostat and was overcome with gratitude to the motel staff, to even the blind reader downstairs, for furnishing such a luxury, as he spotted a compact silver box mounted next to the bathroom door. He raised the thermostat to eighty degrees and turned to his love.

She was in what is called by sleep experts the "runner's position," though Woo was no Freudian and he interpreted this change simply as an opportunity to unlatch and remove the elastic contraption that persisted in keeping her upper half secret from him. Her arms were languid and soft as he pulled them this way and that through the straps. His poor girl was being so good. Whether it was his accurate assessment of the depth of her sleep or his raving desire's rationale, Woo became convinced that Camille would never wake. He moved quickly to her lower half and unrolled her lemon-yellow underpants slowly out and down over her plump curve. He fumbled during the final moments of untangling the yellow bonds from her ankles and feet. When the bonds were free from her body and her body free from its bonds, he turned her from the runner's position so that she was on her back.

He looked at her. He watched her grow cold and stiff and then warm and soft again. He watched her return to the runner's position and pedal her feet and turn her head. He grew self-conscious, and tried to read his magazine in the near dark. This cycle lasted throughout most of the night. He would watch her sleep and then grow self-conscious. He would read his magazine and then grow impatient with its drab articles and idiotic cartoons. He would curse the insufficient light, and then, as if to punish himself, he would read on until he thought he would hurl the magazine at the picture window, and then set it quietly down on the night stand and resume looking at his nubile wife.

During these intervals he was ravenous, and ate both the entire jar of peanuts and the orange, along with a roll of different-colored hard candies that he had found in Camille's toiletry bag. Any chance he may have had of falling asleep was quickly reversed by this massive intake of protein and sugar. The room was hot and smelled of peanuts. In Woo's opinion, a pleasant smell, a comfy cocoon. His pajamas were damp with sweat, but he did not dare remove them. Between his lovely bride and his tasty snacks, his jangled nerves and his exhaustion, the night provided him with a seemingly endless supply of tortured insomniacal bliss. It was not until the sun began to rise over the lake and Camille began to stir that Woo's eyes closed at last. As he fought and then failed to stay awake, he pored over the maps in his head, revised his budget, and thought of the strangeness of the words *honey* and *moon*—were they two words or one? He reviewed the many words he had recently learned: *snow leopard, zebra, flamingo, raspberry, sherbet, Milky Way, prophylactic, Maidenform,* and thought it unlikely that he could possibly remember them all.

He woke at 11:00 A.M., and his first thought was of Pang and the terrible morning he'd slept past eight, a story he'd never told Camille. And then, immediately strengthening his theory that laziness leads to disaster, he heard the sound of his child bride vomiting in the bathroom. Eat too much, he thought. Maybe learn her lesson.

"Camilla," he knocked softly on the bathroom door. "You need some help? Can I get you anything?"

"No," she said whispering. "Please go away. I don't want you to see me. I'm sick."

"Silly girl talking nonsense. Daddy doesn't mind. His poor girl is sick, maybe need something, eh?"

"No, thanks, please go away!" she said urgently.

Woo dressed quickly and went out to buy her some ginger ale, which he found for sale by the can in a vending machine behind the building. He returned to find her in an orange sundress on the floor, tracing the strawberry-red line of the map with her finger. She looked as ripe and as healthy as she had the night before.

"I'm better now," she said, springing up and kissing his cheek. "I just ate too much. I think that's all it was."

"Drink anyway," he opened the can, wiped its aluminum lip, inserted a straw (one of ten he had taken from the restaurant), and handed her the ginger drink.

She sucked on the straw obediently, collapsing her cheeks and puckering her mouth until her sucking noise resonated as air and droplets in the empty can. She was cured instantly.

They spent the day at the beach, on Milky Way Motel towels. Camille lay in her white two-piece bathing suit watching the water, while Woo, hatted and in slacks, sat reading the last of his Chinese newspapers. He refrained from looking at her sun-lotioned body and concentrated instead on conjuring images of her he had on file from the previous night.

The kiss on the cheek this morning had been a puzzle to him. They were not in the habit of touching each other. He thought with pleasure of the possibility that Camille had been awake for part or even all of his late-night roamings, and that the kiss had been a clue to him, an affirmative peck. Now he longed for Iowa, if not for Candy the clerk, and for the day to end and the night to arrive so that he might have a second chance.

"Joseph," Camille pulled her hair back with silver barrette. "Thank you for hanging my clothes up last night. I was so tired."

"Sure, sure. Sleep in your clothes, no good. Not comfortable. Too many wrinkles."

"I really like that you did that."

"You did?" He was alarmed at the possible meanings she intended. "Were you able to sleep?"

"Mmm, like a baby," she tilted her face up to the sky and closed her eyes. "I thought you might be upset with me," she said with her eyes still closed.

"Why upset?"

"Well, you know, it being our honeymoon and all. I sort of slept through it."

"Sleepy girls need their rest, no problem."

"Can I ask you a personal question?"

"You talk nonsense. Anytime ask questions."

"Did I like it?" she asked, sounding intrigued.

"*Shenma* 'like it'? What's the meaning of this question?"

"Do I have to say it? I just mean, you know, did I like *it*?"

"*Shenma* 'it'? What is *it*?"

"What you did to me while I was sleeping."

"Oh my golly, you're some kind of crazy girl! Number one, while you're sleeping I'm reading magazine, have some snacks. No such a thing do to you anything. Number two, you like something you tell me, I'm not telling you! Huh!" he grunted, mildly offended.

"You mean you really just hung my clothes up?" Camille started to laugh.

"What's funny?" Woo demanded. "Of course I'm hanging your clothes up for you. What do you expect?" He sounded shocked, as if the reckless thought of making love to her while she slept had never crossed his ancient, puritanical mind.

There are women who can articulate their wants quite clearly, so that for even the most inexperienced of husbands, supplying those wants becomes easier. And there are men who can, without their wives' lucid articulations, intuit their wants and expertly supply them. Neither Camille nor Woo fit these character types. If just one or the other had been one of those fortunate types, the matter of their lovemaking would have been greatly simplified. But as it was, Camille had never been counted on to articulate anything before, much less something as embarrassingly intimate as her own physical wants, and Woo, a bachelor in the truest, deepest sense of the word, had never before supplied anyone's wants but his own.

This they quickly learned during the series of long nights that unfolded in variously sized Motel 6s across the country. Each was patient with the other afterward. By the grace of her God or his laws, their nights were tender even as they failed to satisfy. But the continuous lack of known demands, coupled with the continuous lack of successful supply, led to a relational revolt that took a toll on their waking hours. Each injured party responded in a different way to the crisis.

Woo lost interest in their evening ritual entirely. That is, he began by feigning a loss of interest that then conveniently turned genuine. Certainly at first, the electrical sensation he'd been experiencing in Camille's presence threatened to derail his celibatic mission, but eventually he found that the longer he ignored his own electricity, the less frequently the voltage flared up. He'd never felt quite so manly and utterly in control before, and was relieved to be rid of that dangerous tangle of live wires—so many variable bolts and sparks and invisible force fields exploding and firing without his permission. Better to maintain control of the charge, to ignite it and snuff it out for his own benefit only.

Camille, on the other hand, became insatiable. Her eyes were fierce slits more often than not, and the many attractions that had delighted Mac's easy Isabelle did not satisfy Woo's impossible bride. No roller coaster was fast enough, no carousel horse the right color. He won carnival game after carnival game, but none of the fun prizes caught her eye. The cotton candy was too sweet, the popcorn too salty, the petting zoo full of nothing but farm animals. "Where are the pandas?" she cried. "Why can't we go dancing?"

She began demanding more and more. She wanted dinners out and movies, museum tickets and dancing—a number of items that were not on their itinerary nor part of their detailed budget. She wanted Iowa City instead of Des Moines, Lake Anita instead of Badger Creek,

Kansas instead of Nebraska. All of it arbitrary, Woo was convinced. All of it designed to madden him. The more she asked for, the more he refused. This he did, not out of spite, but on principle. There were times when he adored her fierceness and longed to turn the car in any direction she wanted to go, but his principles outweighed his adoration for her, and he drove on.

When they arrived at the Motel 6 in Des Moines, she refused to get out of the car. "Why do we always have to stay at Motel 6? I don't want to stay at another one." She had her sandaled feet on the dash to spite him and was looking at the map through the slits of her eyes as if plotting an alternate route.

"Motel 6, what's the problem? We have reservations." Woo didn't understand. What a nice, clean motel! The night before had been particularly tender and unsatisfying, and their daytime personalities were revolting.

"I don't mind staying in a few here and there, but every single time? What will people think?"

"What people?!" Woo shouted, incredulous.

And then, for the first time since their journey west had begun, Camille understood that she was stranded. There were no other people. No Heartland, no mother, no father, no movie dates or trinkets, white rabbits or dried plums—just a husband. She began to cry.

There was nothing, aside from sex and communism, that frightened Woo more than tears, and so while Camille wept over the road atlas, he went into the Motel 6 office and canceled their reservations. He got on Interstate 80 going west and began searching for signs to Lake Anita.

It was at Lake Anita (for which he had silently sacrificed the highly touted Badger Creek) that Woo and Camille encountered a handful of those people whom Camille had unwittingly referred to, just thirty miles earlier, as if her naming of them had made them exist. The incident, which Woo was later loathe to recall in detail, involved a group of four ten-year-old boys who suddenly and in symphony threw wet stones at Woo's sweatered back while he was at the edge of what he thought was a desolate thicket, relieving himself. He was in midstream when the first stone struck, though his sweater cushioned the stone's impact and distracted him from seriously considering its source. Ping! Ping! The second and third struck in quick succession, and then a shower of smaller stones, also wet, hit him like rain. The usual racial epithets were hurled as well, and then as quickly as they had ambushed their man, the boys vanished into the thicket. *Ha ha, ha*, he could hear them, *heh, heh, heh*.

Woo did not let the incident disrupt him. He finished out the stream, shook and tucked himself in, button, then zipper, then belt.

Camille, who had watched through the car windshield, sprang up out of the car when he returned. She rushed up to him and kissed him on the cheek. It was a kiss of the same variety as the kiss on the beach, the sort she spontaneously doled out on rare occasions.

"Why didn't you yell at those lousy jerks?" she asked.

"This is minor incident. Too much trouble for nothing," he said, alluding to a wider spectrum of incidents she knew nothing about.

"Why didn't you at least tell them you aren't Japanese?"

"Why didn't you?" he asked.

She bit her thumbnail and looked down at his sweater, which he had taken off and folded.

"Why were you wearing that sweater?" she wanted to know. "It's so hot! If I was a man, I'd take my shirt off."

"No such a thing. It is unsafe to expose oneself in an isolated location. Hot, cold, doesn't matter."

"Gosh, that's so paranoid," she said. He had looked so funny in that sweater, standing in the August sun.

After the two of them were in the car again, she watched his black eyes scan not just the unknown road in front of them but both mirrors and the shoulders, too. From time to time he looked briefly at her face. She saw then that he too was stranded. No Chinatown, no bachelors, no newspaper, no plums. In the cities and towns to come, who would understand him? Who, if not she, would keep him safe?

So it was that both of them, each marooned in his or her own way, made of the time remaining a temporary life. He drove the car he had given her that she was incapable of driving, and she held in her small lap the many maps he had purchased for his own private pleasure. They ate fresh fruit and dry cereal for breakfast, according to his taste, and they stopped at McDonald's for lunch according to hers. By default, they adhered to Mac Celan's list of restaurants for dinner, less because their tastes correlated with his or Isabelle's and more to prevent disagreement between them. Woo misplaced Celan's list of favorite destinations and it was just as well.

In Nebraska, he bought her a set of checkers, and it became their habit to play in the motel room after dinner. Sometimes while they played, they sipped ginger ale poured from cans into complimentary tumblers filled with complimentary ice. Woo retrieved the ringshaped pieces of ice, which Camille loved to slide on her fingers, from a metal machine every evening. It was Camille's duty to take as many complimentary postcards from the Motel 6 lobby as was appropriate, according to the number available and the apparent disposition of the clerk. When she was bored, which was seldom, she shined his shoes, for he loved his shoes to be shiny but disliked blackening his hands. And when he was feeling tender (also seldom) he ran her a bath.

Their German engine rumbled and coughed, and dust flew through the open windows. They were always in the car unless it was evening, and because of this, Woo felt dirty at the end of each day. She learned that his sweat, like water, had almost no discernible odor; he learned that she hummed while she ate. He sensed at times that she was homesick; she began to suspect that he dyed his hair. Both grew accustomed to the sound of traffic roaring past them, the sounds of "people" motoring swiftly and mysteriously past them, even as they slept. The bright red-orange 6 became a beacon to both, though it meant something different to each of them. They exhausted their supply of prophylactics and did not buy more. It was difficult to connect that which they did in the dark with their nomadic sunlit selves.

Their conversations quieted and then ceased, and that was for both of them an unexpected comfort. And then one morning they crossed the California state line, and Woo said, "Tonight we will be home." And Camille said, not without a sadness, that she had lost track of the days, and in so doing, had almost forgotten where it was they were going.

*I don't know now if my sister Sue was singing or screaming,
and it appears I didn't know then, either, already off in my
own world at age two. My mother still takes it all in stride.*

Lucy Honig's collection, *The Truly Needy and Other Stories*, won the 1999 Drue
Heinz Prize and was published by University of Pittsburgh Press. Another collection, *Open Season*, was published in 2002 by Scala House. She teaches in the graduate program in international health at Boston University's School of Public Health.

MULTIPLE LISTINGS

Lucy Honig

"Geez," says the red guy, the talker, "where is this Babe anyway?" We're waiting for B. Abe Gernardi, Realtor, who I'm ready to bet doesn't exist. If you're for real and you've got a water-view apartment going for a hundred grand, even if it's only a minuscule one-bedroom, you don't keep canceling appointments with buyers who claim to be so interested, especially those of us coming up from the South Shore. It's almost three weeks now since I first tried to set this up, and the market being what it is, with most places snapped up in a day, I gotta wonder: doesn't he really want to sell it? Is B. Abe's Realty for real, and is the condo?

Not that with this client of mine I have a likely buyer here. She has the old champagne-taste-on-a-wine-budget problem: a "middling" teacher's salary, that's how she puts it, and lots of debt since a divorce two years ago, but she's got to have a water view and still be on a subway line. She saw water back in the good days with the ex, which I gather were not too numerous, a window on sunny times that opened briefly and then slammed shut again about halfway through the marriage. But even when I find these cheaper glimpses of water for her, something's always wrong: too small, too big, too far from something, too close to something, too shabby, too noisy, too many planes flying too low overhead on the way in or out of Logan. She'll never buy, of this I'm pretty sure. She walks into a place hunting for the reasons not to. She'll drag me to hell and back a million times before she figures it out herself: plunking money down on her own dismal, solitary future is just not an appealing investment.

"Aren't your feet freezing?" she asks, staring at my bare ankles, my clogs. Then she honks her nose into a ratty handkerchief. She's had a cold for just about as long as I've known her, which is nearly a year now. "If you want to go home, just say the word."

"I'm fine," I assure her. But *you*, I want to say: get rid of that cold. Pull yourself together. Forget that skunk of an ex-husband and go meet someone else. Stop calling yourself Patty and get a grown-up name. Dye your hair or at least rinse out the gray. And just get over it! I've done it twice myself; it's not so bad.

A bone-piercing wind whips right off the harbor and howls up the street. It's so drizzly and foggy, no way will we see if the "magnificent harbor view" exists or not—if we ever get into the apartment, which by now I'm pretty sure we never will. We're huddled in front of the brownstone on Webster Street where the four-story row houses, in semi-gentrified repair, are painted pleasing colors. We've been waiting for a quarter of an hour now, not just me and my client and the red guy and his mother and their agent, who were here first, but now an off-duty transit cop, still in uniform, and a frizzy blond with a cell phone glued to her ear. The red guy, wearing only a lightweight jacket, gets redder in the cold; you'd think for sure he was Irish, but his mother doesn't speak a word of English. She must have taken the boat from Palermo forty years ago or more, like mine, but he's still got to translate for her.

I redial B. Abe and leave another message. "This is Angie from Winners All Realty *again*. A *lot* of us are *still* waiting for you, Mr. Gernardi."

What kind of realtor gives the exact same appointment time to four different parties? Talk about chutzpah. If he wanted an open house, he should have had it on a Sunday afternoon, not at 6 P.M. on a dark dank Tuesday night. Now going on 6:20.

"So Joe Peroni's closing the shop, did ya hear?" says Red to no one in particular. "I used to do his plumbing."

"Oh yeah? Time to retire, I guess," says the transit cop.

"And move to Florida," says Red. "The lucky dog."

"So go down there and look for a place for your mom," says his agent. "I could put you in contact with one of our people in Sarasota."

He gazes down at his mother, who is gray, not red, then plants a sloppy kiss on her forehead. She is completely bewildered. "Don't worry, Mama, I'll never send you to Florida."

"Florida," she says, brightening; and then out come English words: "Very nice, Florida. Andiamo."

The phone woman, who has been standing a couple of doors down from us, finally closes up her svelte Nokia and moves toward our huddle, a little wobbly on insanely high-heeled shoes. But then her phone rings again and as she answers she turns away from us.

"Tomorrow? Not on your life," she says testily.

"Hey, is that Babe?" Red yells to her.

"Mr. Gernardi, you mean," his agent corrects him, while she hands me her card with a fancy Rowe's Wharf address. Specialist in North End properties, it boasts, but here she is in scruffy Eastie. She herself has seen better days. Her lipstick is smudged and it's all I can do to keep from dabbing at her chin with kleenex.

Red yells louder, as if Phone Woman didn't hear him. "You got Babe on the phone there?"

She swivels back around to us and with her free hand swats Red's question away. Glaring at Red, she shouts into her little phone, "For Chrissakes, find Jake no matter where the hell he is before you make another move."

"That's not B. Abe Gernardi she's talking to," says the transit cop. "I'm pretty sure."

Red's mother mumbles in Italian.

"He'll be here in a minute, Mama," Red says to her, though really to us, because he says it again in Italian so she'll understand. Maybe if we all said it in a different language we'd believe it. "That might be him on the phone."

Phone Woman is furious. "We'll worry about *that* when the time comes. First you gotta find Jake."

The transit cop says, "Nope, she ain't talking to Babe. Must be a private conversation."

The North End realtor shakes her head. "The world today. Every-one on the phone, they don't look where they're going."

Red paces impatiently in a small circle. Then he turns to my client. "Have you been looking for a condo long?"

Rattled from her solitude—social graces aren't her forte—Patty shrugs uneasily. Will she admit she's been looking for a year? Nope. "Off and on for a while. And you?"

"Just started. It's for *her*." He pats his mother on the head. "Me, I'll stay where I am, a coupla blocks over there." He whips his head back, to suggest somewhere behind him. "But this afternoon we saw a place there—" he gestures with a chapped freckled hand toward the harbor, meaning the North End. "What a place, let me tell you. They're ask-ing $319,000. Beautiful, beautiful, and everything you could ask for, even a twenty-four-hour concierge." He pronounces it "conserge." "Balcony, jacuzzi, icemaker, wall-to-wall, everything, parking—and she don't even drive. But it wasn't so big. One bedroom, medium size. Sheesh. Three hundred nineteen thousand dollars."

I can't get my mind around this: how could they be looking at both *that* apartment and *this* one? What on earth is their budget? What on earth is their agent doing?

"Wow!" says Patty. "*I* couldn't afford that."

A trickle of pedestrians thickens now and then to a steady stream as trains disgorge at Maverick Square. Secretary types, blue-collar types, a suited yuppie here and there. A woman wearing a Muslim headscarf rushes past, dragging by hand a child who struggles to keep up. A gaggle of Spanish-speaking laborers saunters by in no great hurry. Then a few more yuppies march along, clearly to a very different drummer: young dot-com people, money traders, computer kids.

I look at the yuppies and say, "The wave of the future."

"Oh yes, this is a very up-and-coming place," says Red's agent. "In a year or two, you won't recognize it."

"Better buy now, huh?" says the transit cop.

My phone rings and everyone hushes; it *is* B. Abe. "It's for us," I announce. The others raise a cheer. "You hear how happy this crowd is to hear from you, Mr. Gernardi?"

"Call me Babe," he says.

"We sure do hope you're on your way," I reply.

He assures me he's just around the corner and will be with us pronto.

So we keep a lookout. A car slows down, but it's not him, then another, and still not him. We keep waiting. An elderly blue-haired woman emerges from our building and Red pounces. In two seconds we know she's from the top floor, right above our condo.

"See, she can do it," says Red to his mother. "The stairs won't be so hard."

The North End agent says, "An elevator never hurts, but neither does good exercise."

"At least she wouldn't have a heavy tread, walking around upstairs. That's a plus." My client is musing aloud; I've been privy to these conversations with herself before. "But she's old; she could die or go into a nursing home. Noisy, heavy-footed people could replace her. A possible sudden resale upstairs, that's a definite minus." She scribbles in her notebook, enters one more minus in a ledger she keeps on each place we see.

I nudge her to the brighter side; this is my role. "If you buy that one too, when it opens up, you'd have a two-story place, an even more fantastic view."

She scowls.

"Okay, so maybe things will change. A promotion. A rich boyfriend. Maybe you'll win the lottery."

"Oh sure. You think I waste my money on those tickets?"

I am stymied now. What can you say to someone who doesn't leave room for the unexpected?

And then a silver Lexus that has turned the corner and quietly snuck up on us comes to a stop. A short, stout, half-balding and sharply dressed man of about forty gets out, leaving the Lexus double parked. He tugs at his suit jacket to uncrease it, straightens the black tie on his black shirt.

"Babe, how ya doin'?" the transit cop calls to him.

A sleek PT Cruiser double parks behind the Lexus, and a tall, thin, weasel-eyed guy emerges. This is Paulie, B. Abe's sidekick, who I've talked to on the phone. They quickly shake hands with us and we identify ourselves. B. Abe pointedly winks at me twice as he apologizes for being late.

"But folks, believe me," he says, flashing a smile, then eyeing Paulie impatiently. Paulie shuffles through a massive and fully stocked key ring like the warden at San Quentin must once have had. "Just wait 'til you see this."

"We waited already," the North End agent replies curtly. And we wait a minute more while Paulie finds the key.

We tromp single file up two flights to the third floor. Now there are nine of us: B. Abe and his sidekick in the lead, Red and his mother right behind them, the North End realtor and I bringing up the rear. The stairs are unusually narrow and steep, twisting not exactly in a spiral: they're more gemelli than rotini in shape. My own ample hips just barely fit within the width of them, and the transit cop has to maneuver himself sideways on the curves. The phone woman's teetering high heels and my client's sensible rubber-soled flats clomp above me.

"The movers would have some hell of a time getting my living-room pieces up here," says Phone Woman. "Not to mention the king-size bed."

Red's mother pauses on the second floor landing to catch her breath and lets the rest of us pass by.

"Take your time, Mrs. Santini," says the transit cop, keeping her company, while Red trudges ever upward.

"It's not so bad," says Red from near the top. "You can make it, Mama." Sure she can, at least this once. But is he *really* thinking of putting her here for good?

"Who lives on the second floor?" Patty asks. Years ago, sometime before the good days, I think, a rock band moved in next door and left her permanently scarred.

"Nobody," calls down Paulie. "Been vacant for years."

"Who owns it?" I ask.

"Don't know."

"Hmmph," I say aloud. "What's the deal with this building any-how?" It's hard to believe there isn't a square residential inch in this whole city you couldn't make a fortune from these days if you just gave it a coat of paint. There's no such thing as a vacancy in Boston anymore—except this second floor here.

When we get to the top of the stairs at our floor, each of us in turn stops still at the open apartment doorway for a moment, like we're about to parachute jump out of a plane and need to center ourselves and say a little prayer first. Each of us in turn finally takes the leap. God help us, all nine of us squeeze in.

This is the first apartment I have ever seen that's been bonsaied; it's a doll house. Adjusting to the size of it is like adjusting to a different light; after a while you just *do*. What was it that Alice ate in Wonderland to make her smaller? I don't remember, but whatever it was, we desperately need some here. We trip over each other, trying to move from room to room.

"Is this adorable or what?" gushes B. Abe. "Talk about potential!" He flings out his arms to encompass the vast potential, and winds up belting Paulie in the gut.

The little kitchen with its little appliances is neat as a pin and gleaming. B. Abe is still on top of us in here. "It could easily be an eat-in kitchen if you just opened up that corner."

I poke at the worn maroon velours drapes, which might have been salvaged from an old theater, find the opening, and lean inside. Patty and Red's mother stick their heads in, too. This corner of the kitchen has been made into a miniature bedroom, filled entirely by a bed; a pink-and-purple-striped taffeta-like frilled bedspread is graced with half a dozen beanie babies. The headboard is one kitchen wall, and a bleeding Christ on a crucifix hangs from it; the maroon drapes wall in one side and the foot; ruffled orange curtains frame a window in the fourth wall, and a dark green shade is drawn over it. From that window you'd probably have a super view, but obviously whoever lives here wants neither to see out or be seen.

I back out through the drapes and bump into the transit cop, step-ping on his toe. When he steps back to get away from me, he crashes

into Phone Woman. They both have to step out of the kitchen altogether to let Patty and Red's mother and me maneuver to the bathroom. Here pink plastic flowers adorn everything, including what
appears to be a small shrine atop the toilet reservoir: pictures of saints,
candles, incense. Red is already inspecting the shower. "Needs caulk-
ing," he says, then does a little dance with me on the pink shag rug so
I can get back there and he can exit. I flush the toilet. Hovering in the
doorway, Patty can reach the sink taps and turn them on. "Low pressure," she says. She steps back, Red's mother steps in. She turns on the
taps, too, in imitation, watches the water and shrugs.

Next we make our way into the living room. I squeeze past the
North End realtor, who whispers to Patty confidentially: "It's very
cute in here." A cell phone rings, and Phone Woman steps into the
bathroom to talk. The transit cop, who'd been in there, bolts out. B.
Abe, meanwhile, keeps up a running patter, pointing out all the
gentry-friendly features—the hardwood floor, built-in china cabinet, tilt-in windows, central air. He transfixes us with detail. So at
first I don't even notice those *other* people in the room, who B. Abe
never seems to see at all. Two adults, four children: a family, squeezed
onto a small sofa and a loveseat, clinging for dear life to one another. A dark-skinned tableau of silent fear. They might as well be
inside a painting on the wall, for all anybody else pays attention to
them. But they're real-life, flesh-and-blood, three-dimensional, quiv-
ering human beings. The tenants. They live here. They cast glances
furtively at the crowd: which of us will eventually evict them?
Where will they go then?

As everyone mills around, heading toward a real bedroom with a
door, I say hello. The father eyes me warily. "Hello, buenas tardes," he
replies, with a short burst of smile that quickly vanishes. I retreat.

Patty is shooting questions in the little bedroom, where two beds,
two dressers, and an armoire have somehow all been squeezed in. "Is
there hardwood underneath this carpeting?"

Paulie pries up a corner of the carpet with a screwdriver. "Looks
like yes."

"How about utilities? What do gas and electric run a month?"

"I don't know," says B. Abe, "but if you're really interested, I'll find out."

She taps an exterior wall. "Any insulation here?"

B. Abe shrugs.

"And how's the roof? When was it last redone? What's it made of?" She's very practiced now in asking questions. "Any special assessments lately?"

B. Abe rolls his eyes, lands his look on me, and winks. "Again, if you want to pursue it, I'll get the information. No problem. Have Angie here gimme a call."

Patty and I squeeze past Red, his mother, and his agent, who are pow-wowing in the bedroom doorway, and make our way through the living room just as a pink-cheeked young couple appears, probably dot-com kids, apologizing for being late. That makes eleven of us in here now. Seventeen if you count the tenants. But not for long: the new arrivals take one quick look and head back down the stairs. B. Abe Gernardi has the gall to frown with disapproval.

"B. Abe," I say, carefully separating the B. from the Abe into two annoying syllables, "how can you deliberately show an apartment this size to so many people all at once?"

"C'mon," he says to me, with a wink. "Would *you* wanna keep coming back here?" He watches me lead Patty to the deck, where no one else has ventured.

Sure enough, when you look from out here toward what must be the harbor, all you can see is a thick, impenetrable gray wad of woolly fog. Not even the lights of downtown Boston a quarter of a mile away can pierce this stuff; they emit only a sickly muted glint. Logan Airport, behind us, is ominously quiet.

"There's supposed to be a water view out there somewhere," I say.

"Well, at least planes aren't landing or taking off on this side." Patty strikes an unusually positive note.

"Oh honey," I reply. "They just can't go anywhere in this fog."

Then B. Abe bursts onto the deck and gestures sweepingly out toward the wall of fog; his hand disappears in it. "Look at that great view of the skyline, those bright lights, the water, the sailboats. Porpoises, too, they got in there now. Aren't you just gonna love it, cocktails and barbecues out here?" This guy's enough to make me want to change professions.

Patty starts questioning again. "Who owns the vacant lots beside the docks? I saw them when I was walking around." She always does her homework first: tests out the ride on public transportation, moseys through the neighborhood.

"That's Massport here"—he signals vaguely in one direction—"and some developer *there*"—he signals in another.

"So somebody's gonna build on that parcel where theoretically there's a view now."

"I think it's been in the courts."

"Sooner or later somebody's gonna build there," she repeats. For once I can picture her in a classroom, fully in charge. "Up, I'd guess. They'll build *up* into the air. It's so rare these days that new buildings get built *down*."

"Honest, I'm not sure about the plans for that property." B. Abe is having trouble now; Patty's sarcasm catches him off guard. Me too. "At this point in time, I mean. I can find that out if you really want."

Poised with pen to notebook, Patty says, "It's Boston. Eventually they get what they want. They'll build up, and the view will be wiped out." Then she scribbles on her balance sheet. I can feel the scale tipping irrevocably to the minus.

Then back inside I wait in one corner, out of everyone's path, as Patty squeezes through each room once more, though I can't imagine why: isn't it clear by now, this place is not for her? She peeks into cupboards, paces off lengths, takes notes, and sketches diagrams. "Look! Another closet!" She pulls hopefully at a doorknob in the living room, only to be face to face with a gas furnace.

"Oh," she says, disappointed. "Ugh. There could be fumes from this."

Just then, wouldn't you know it, the furnace comes to life, kicking on with a hiss and a snap and a heavy thump, culminating in a steady roar. Startled, Patty jumps back. But the tenant mother puts her hands to her ears and lets out a terrifying whimper.

This to me does not seem like a normal reaction. Nor to anyone else: a hush falls over the apartment, and we buyers all stand and gawk as the mother sobs quietly, holding an ornately embroidered little pillow against her face. The older daughter, about twelve, tries to comfort her, but the baby shrieks, insisting she hold him instead. The father has put each arm around the other kids, as if to shield them; they burrow their heads into his shoulders. The mother's sobs intensify, and the baby wails at the top of his lungs.

There's really no denying that they're there now, but we all still act as if they're not. Red says, "I never checked the kitchen sink," and heads that way, his mother and agent in tow. Phone Woman punches in some numbers and retreats to the bathroom to talk. "I don't get such a good signal here," she calls out. B. Abe and Paulie schmooze with the transit cop in the bedroom.

But Patty stays right where she is beside the furnace and says something in Spanish. The mother puts down her pillow. The father says something in reply. The kids wriggle from his clutch and sit up. The baby stops crying, eyes fixed on Patty. They all go back and forth for a while in rapid-fire Spanish. Then Patty crouches beside the mother and gives her a tissue to dry her face. She clasps the woman's hand in both her own and rattles off a whole long speech; I haven't got a clue what she's saying. The older boy shoves over and makes room for her, patting the cushion he frees up. She sits there, pressed between two kids. She takes the baby on her lap and dandles him. The younger daughter pulls out what must be her homework and hands it to Patty proudly. Patty pretends to read it upside down. They laugh a little, they *ooh* and *ah* a little, they gaze warmly at each other as if they've discovered some long-lost connection. They talk and talk. I barely recognize my client: her face is so animated, like she's just shed the last ten years.

And the family, suddenly they're not on the brink of eviction and catastrophe; suddenly they're home. And I can't imagine what the rest of us are doing here. 🕴

I asked my mother for photos, and she sent me three. In two I am armed—this and another showing me with a sword, astride a wheeled zebra. In the third I am clutching a doctor's bag. Go figure.

Paul Michel was born in Philadelphia, grew up mostly in Ohio, and now lives in Seattle. He is a graduate of Kenyon College and of the Warren Wilson MFA Program for Writers. His stories and poetry have appeared in *Anthology, Crania, Fan,* the *Red Rock Review,* and the *Best of Rosebud.* "Say to the Waves" won first place in the Writers Workshop 2001 Fiction Contest.

SAY TO THE WAVES

Paul Michel (signature)

Paul Michel

I

At three o'clock in the afternoon of February 26, Gerta Olsen's husband Shorty dove headfirst off the twelfth-floor balcony of the Norview Senior Center. The back of his skull exploded against a concrete parking berm, within full view of the reception desk. Three residents and a twenty-two-year-old Norview volunteer saw Shorty hit the pavement. Gerta was in her kitchen at the time, making a triple shortbread recipe for the day's Community Tea. Until she heard the screams from the lobby, she had no sense that anything was wrong.

February 26 was a God-awful, wet, windy day. Every day had been this way (every blessed day, Gerta was sure of it) since the last week of September. Yet even on the gloomiest days, with no letup in the downpour and a sky the color of dirt, Shorty had claimed—from his armchair—that it didn't bother him. No way. He'd been a fisherman most of his life, chasing salmon, herring, and halibut in frigid waters from Coos Bay to Kodiak and beyond. A fisherman who minds the weather, he told Gerta, is no fisherman at all.

If not the rain, then why? What to say to her Norview neighbors, flocked like pigeons at her door, wanting to know how and when and what could they do, but mostly why, why, why?

"He was in God's hands at that moment," she told them. But this didn't satisfy them any more than it did her.

It wasn't the weather. It was nothing to do with his health—at least not that she knew of. There must have been something else. Each day she tried to think what. Was it because he was on the balcony looking out, and he didn't want to turn around again and look in? But no, she thought. There must be more to it than that. There must be.

The rain let up, eventually. It always did by midsummer, though this year it held on well past the Fourth. A dry day dawned at last during the third week of July. Broadcast weathermen warned of sun. Gerta, half-awake in an unfamiliar morning glare, ran her fingers over the smooth cotton sheets beside her, and at that moment came upon the idea of the bench.

The reaction at Norview was lukewarm. Another bench. Tillie Fosterbach had a wrought-iron bicycle rack designed in her husband's honor, and placed outside the NutraLife store on Market Street. Fran Steinbacher commissioned a drinking fountain for hers. Vivian Bulberg adopted an elk herd near Wenatchee, and named it after her dear departed Bucky, who'd died on a hunt, shotgun in hand. Benches were so—well, sedentary, in this day and age. So predictable.

"I wonder," said Vivian.

"Do you think?" asked Edna Hamsun.

"I suppose it's an idea," said Dr. Lauber, who came by on Thursdays. Gerta decided to move forward on her own.

She and Shorty had a son, Eric, a childless, fifty-year-old widower with a torso the size of a hot-water tank. He managed a small shipyard near the Ballard Locks, a seat-of-the-pants place where ancient tugs and trawlers came to be beaten into their last feeble years of service before scrapping. He had not been especially close to Shorty, nor in any particular way estranged. At least not that Gerta was aware of. But then, he seldom spoke his mind.

"I will build you a bench," he said.

What he constructed was beautiful. It was not wood, not in this climate, but a black, feather-light, composite material made in Alaska out of waste tires and used engine oil. A substance that would last forever. He molded it to resemble a breaching Orca whale, its back arched high in the center, its curved seat like black waves beneath. When Gerta presented its design to the Art in Parks Council, the judges saw a tiny woman with eyes like jewels, wearing a pale yellow blouse and a snow-white cardigan. They couldn't have said no to her, besides which they had raved over Eric's sketches.

"Can he do more?" they asked.

"There can only be one," she said.

The Council picked a stunning site: Golden Gardens Park, north of the Shilshole Bay Marina. It had a straight-ahead view of the blue and snowy Olympic Mountains, with the gray waters of Puget Sound between. Ferries, tankers, and fat, slow freighters passed by all day long in the fog-bound distance. Sea lions barked on the buoys near shore. Gulls swooped and screamed. It was a postcard come to life.

Gerta and Shorty had been to the park together once, the summer before. Shorty had stood on the sidewalk path that looped behind the brick Rec Center, while Gerta sat alone on a massive driftwood log, barley a spit from the nudging waves. A flotilla of racing skiffs passed by. Their sails shone with all the rainbow colors, catching the sun as well as the wind and making full, bright use of both.

"Did you see the boats?" she asked, when they were back in their Buick and headed up the shoelace hill to Ballard. "Sailing." He made a sound like a stifled sneeze. She waited. "Damned rich-man's hobby. Might as well stand in the shower and rip up hundred dollar bills," he added. As she knew he would.

The bench was finished by the end of the following March. It had been just over a year since Shorty's death. There was a sunrise dedication service at the park. Attending were Gerta, Eric, and Vivian Bulberg. Dr. Lauber arrived late, as a drizzle was starting to fall.

"A beautiful bench," he said. "Shorty would be proud."

"Yes," said Gerta. She hoped so. She truly did.

II

Danny Jansen was unemployed. There was a reason: he couldn't stand being told what to do. This meant that holding onto a job, any kind of job, seemed to him an exercise in basic self-denial. He was twenty-one years old. His father Bert had held the same job for more than thirty years. He was a photographer for the Seattle Police Department. He

shot crime scenes and accidents; suspects and evidence. And corpses.
"You learn to live with it," he said. Well, yeah, thought Danny. That's
exactly the problem.

Lots of guys in Ballard besides Danny had time on their hands.
They knew each other, more or less, from high school or sports, though
not many were really close friends. Nearly all were white guys, and all
but a few still lived at home. Nobody had a girlfriend, at least not for
more than a few weeks off and on, which was also about as long as
any of them ever held onto a job. They'd gather at one park or another, during the day when there was nobody around but bums and
retirees and moms with real small kids, and a minimum of cops driving by slowly, looking for trouble where there was none, really.

Golden Gardens was their favorite. It was big, and hardly ever crowded,
and way at the north end the sand petered out in a tumble of huge, gray
rocks with lots of shadows and moss-slick cubbies where a couple of
guys could get out of the wind and sneak a joint and maybe a cold can
of Rainier, which warmed a body up surprisingly well on a blustery day.
A pair of Burlington Railroad tracks ran along a low bluff above the
beach. Amtrak coaches passed by sometimes, but what Danny and his
friends loved best were the freight trains—the five-diesel, half-mile
monsters with their black tankers, their box cars of blue and green,
maybe a flash of forest when an empty flatbed blinked by. Then more
flatbeds, muscled high with raw, yellow lumber, stenciled pink and blue.
Some of the guys talked of riding them, like the old timers they'd heard
about, going south to California or east to Montana and the high
country. A few of the guys said they had, but nobody believed them.

Brian was a gawky boy, with a buzz cut and an earring, and a botched
tattoo of a dragon on his inner left arm. He was a dentist's son who
lived up on the high hills above the park. He claimed to have ridden
an empty boxcar with a buddy all the way to Spokane.

"They go real slow sometimes," he said. "We just ran alongside and
jumped on."

"Then what?" asked Steve. With his ponytail and Yankees cap, Steve
was the one who was always saying, Next week I'm outta here.

"We rode," said Brian. "We crouched by the door and smoked a number, and the world went whizzing by. It was awesome. You're real close to the tracks so it seems even faster."

"And what did you do when it was time to get off?"

"We just, you know, waited for a soft place and jumped off."

"You are so full of shit." Steve tossed a can out into the waves, which pushed it right back toward shore.

"What do you know?" said Bryan. "You've never been anywhere."

"I've been to Spokane. The train doesn't even *go* through Spokane."

"Yeah, well, fuck you."

Danny wasn't so sure. Not about where the train went—he had no idea. But it didn't seem such an outrageous idea to jump one, and then jump off someplace so different you'd hardly even remember where you came from.

He'd had five different jobs between Christmas and April, and still spent most days wandering down to the park. The guys would laugh when he showed up, fresh from quitting another burger place or getting kicked off a carpet-cleaning crew.

"Here comes Mr. Career," somebody would say, handing him a cold one.

"Ah, shit," he'd reply, and everyone knew just what he meant.

Just after Easter, he took a late-shift job at a book warehouse down in SoDo. Long nights, shit pay, pushing a shopping cart up and down aisles the length of airplane hangers, filling orders for computer customers as far away as Amsterdam and Argentina. The air in the place was thick with dust, and the towering shelves held as many rats as books. The other workers, temps like himself, were all nerves and attitude, pumped up on coffee and cigarettes, and thinking up ways to tell their friends about the hell hole they'd survived. Danny lasted a week. His super caught him filling a textbook order for a high school in Nebraska with two dozen copies of *The Illustrated Weird Sex Bible*, the week's second-best seller.

Danny was the seventeenth temp fired that night. On his way to the bus stop he walked next to a tall guy about his age, a fidgety sort who kept looking back over his shoulder at the warehouse as if it was something that might follow them.

Paul Michel

"Bullshit fucking place," the big guy finally said, shoving his hands into his jacket pockets.

"You got that right," said Danny. Daylight was breaking. It was raining hard again, and cold. The big guy's black rubber boots hit the puddles like canoe paddles. He had his pants tucked inside them, like something from a TV show about Scotland. Every step splattered dirty water up to the knees of Danny's jeans.

"Jesus," he said, jumping out of the way. "What the fuck you got on your feet?"

"Sorry," the big guy answered. "I got these for fishing. It's the only way to make any money. Everything else is bullshit."

"So why did you quit?"

The big guy looked down. His eyes were bloodshot, his hair was wet and stringy, and his pimply nose was hooked like a hammer's back end.

"I got kicked off the boat for smoking weed. It's my brother's boat. He's some kind of Christian or something." He made a rough sound in his throat, then spat into a puddle. "Fuck him. I'm going back out this summer. There are plenty of boats."

"Gotta be better than that," said Danny, meaning the warehouse.

"Fucking starving is better than that. Fucking knocking off mini-marts is better than that."

"You got that right," Danny said again.

The big guy's bus came first. He turned on the top step and raised his head.

"You oughtta fish," he said. "I'm tellin' you."

Danny's bus went all the way to Golden Gardens. He was the last to get off. A fat man with a thin beard, no coat, and a black dog on a leash passed him on his way down from the stop, running hard the other way, toward the parking lot. Otherwise he was alone.

The rain was steady, the fog thick. He couldn't see the orange buoys close to shore. He could barely make out the bluff where the trains ran. Except for the trash in the sand—a tennis-racket head, a scattered deck of cards, the leg of a plump pink doll—he could almost imagine himself a pioneer, walking the waterfront in its pristine, uncorrupted

106   *Glimmer Train Stories*

state. Far out on the water there sounded a foghorn's moan. It might have been the pure sound of sadness itself.

Not far from the sheltering rocks, there emerged a shape from the mist that Danny hadn't seen before: a low wooden platform, right there in the middle of the dune grass and driftwood, just beyond the high-tide line. It was the size of a small room, gleaming with fresh planks and shiny new nails, even in the rain. Along one edge was a bench, facing the water. It was a wild-looking thing, its curved seat black and smooth, its back a fat arc in the shape, Danny saw, of a breaching whale. He looked slowly behind him, then all around, but he was the only living thing in view. When he stepped up on the platform his boots made a hollow sound on the planks. The bench was sleek and slippery, not wood or concrete or metal, but something molded, or beaten, maybe, into shape. He sat down.

Over the water the fog was starting to lift. The weather to the west had risen above the mountains, so that their peaks glowed white against a deep, distant gray, with the clouds settling along their tops like a torn cotton blanket. Shapes appeared: boats, more than Danny imagined would have braved such pea-soup conditions. Maybe it wasn't so bad out there on the water. A tug pulled a tall crane on a barge. A giant cruise ship, bound for Alaska, looked like a bath toy in the distant waves. Closer in a fleet of trawlers hurried by, summoned by some breathless rumor of fish.

Danny wondered if any of the Nebraska shipment had gotten out of the mailroom before the super tracked it down. Fucking idiot. Fucking job. He leaned forward, his chin cupped in his hands. Between his boots was a steel plaque, bolted to the wet planks: *Shorty Olsen*, it read. There were smaller letters below: *In Memory of a Fisherman*. He looked up and glanced around, as if suddenly a person or maybe a dog had made a noise in the tall grass. But nothing moved except the waves.

III

Gerta met Shorty in high school—not in Seattle, but in a North Dakota prairie town called Botkins. Her parents had emigrated from Norway at the turn of the century, settling on the high plains to raise grains and dairy cattle. This they managed, barely, for almost fifty years, until they died of simple weariness within six winter weeks of each other. Gerta and Shorty were long since gone by then. They journeyed back east for the funeral, but Botkins had by this time become little more to them than the place they'd left. They didn't stay long enough to unpack.

Shorty's real name was Einar, though no one in Seattle except Gerta (and Eric) ever knew this. His parents also came from Norway, and also to farm. They were killed by a hard winter flu when Shorty was a toddler. He was raised by aunts and older cousins, the runt of the Olsen litter, passed around like a difficult houseplant that no one could quite persuade to bloom. In high school he turned a little wild, a little reckless, and young Gerta found this fetching in a town whose few teenage boys could hardly look a girl in the eye and not stutter. Three days after his eighteenth birthday, the news came from Pearl Harbor. Shorty enlisted, but the Army declared him too small for combat. He spent the war behind a series of identical battered steel desks in North Carolina, Louisiana, Ohio, and finally Fort Lewis, Washington. When the fighting was over he took a train back to Botkins. He found Gerta at her parents' house and asked her to marry him and move to Seattle, where he planned to fish for salmon with some Swedes and Norwegians he'd met during his service. Gerta teased him, saying sure, why not, she had never seen the ocean. Shorty said that he was grateful to her, for waiting out the war till he returned. She didn't remind him that the only men left in Botkins during the long war years were either old, deaf, blind, or all three. Instead she called him her hero, and he laughed.

As it happened, Seattle was not on the ocean. Gerta was surprised. She had imagined wide beaches, blue horizons, and the brisk smell of the sea. Instead she found rain and clammy fog, with stark mountains playing peek-a-boo between the ever-present clouds. And a smell not so much of the sea, but of fish. Shorty joined one crew, then another, sailing for many nervous weeks and months away while Gerta nursed a tiny baby girl who died in diapers, then raised a chunky boy who didn't laugh even when you tickled him. Shorty spent his shore time planning and pacing, killing days in Market Street taverns and mowing their miniature Ballard lawn, its trees pruned trim and tidy.

Above the McPherson's Realty calendar in the kitchen, Gerta tacked a yellow newspaper clipping, taped to a half-sheet of blue construction paper. She snipped it from the *Post Intelligencer* the second season Shorty went fishing, from an article about Ballard's annual Blessing of the Fleet. (She avoided the Blessing itself—there were too many widows there who needed a look in the eye she couldn't quite give them.) During the first two decades that Shorty fished, Gerta reread the clipping every time she checked to see how long till he returned. It was titled "The Fisherman's Prayer:"

Oh God, whose way is the sea and whose path is in the great waters, guide all who fish and travel the ways of the trackless deep.

If the storms come, guide them safely through to the haven they would reach. Say to the waves, "Peace. Be still." You hold the hearts of people in the hollow of your hand. Amen.

Often she had wondered who the Prayer was really for. The men on the boats? Or the women and children on shore? She said this to Eric once on the telephone, not long after he'd moved out on his own, on a nervous morning when Shorty hadn't called at his appointed time from Sitka.

"You get delayed sometimes," Eric said. He had tried one outing with the fleet, but his stomach couldn't stand the ceaseless rocking.

"There's a radio on the boat," she countered.

"Ma, that's for emergencies."

"This isn't an emergency?"

"It's an emergency when the Coast Guard comes. This is an inconvenience."

"How do we know where the Coast Guard is today? How do we know they're not on their way right now?"

"He's a few hours late, Ma. Relax. He'll call."

He did call, the next day, delayed as Eric said. After their abbreviated conversation about overdue bills and upcoming taxes, Gerta took the clipping off the wall and put it in the back of a loose-leaf scrapbook. There it stayed for more than twenty years. The day she returned from burying Shorty (Eric drove her home, but did not come inside), she dug out the Prayer and hung it back over the calendar. The tack hole in the plaster was still open. The construction paper had faded, and the clipping was golden with age, but the tape still held strong.

IV

The sinking of the *Laura Lee* hit Ballard like a fist. Not that the community hadn't lost men at sea before. Since 1895, more than a hundred years earlier, there had not been a single season when the entire fleet came back, man for man. Everyone who sailed knew this for fact. Those left behind knew it even better. But the *Laura Lee* was no isolated wreck or drowning—it was the loss of ten men on a 150-foot crab boat in a Bering Sea so rough it nearly claimed a would-be rescue helicopter with its ice-hammer, skyscraping waves. News of the sinking was a prime-time event, with startling photos from the chopper and nervous TV crews on the shores of the vicious waters, saying nothing that could help. There was not a single survivor.

It was even worse than that. In the several weeks following the accident, six of the crew bodies turned up on beaches from Akut Island to Bristol Bay, born by winds and waves like ghastly notes in bottles, mocking the misery of those who wished for their departed at least the honor of being lost at sea. One by one the bodies were flown home: bloated, mangled, mauled by bears, chewed by sea lions, and made almost unrecognizable by the elements that had claimed them. With each discovery the living cried *Enough*.

The last body to be flown to Seattle was that of Danny Jansen. The *Laura Lee* had been his first sailing, and the newspapers made much of this: A graduate of Ballard High, a trombone player in the marching band, a "nice kid" to the couple of teachers who remembered more than his name. The Saturday before the funeral, the morning paper ran a headline article, "The Men We Send to Sea," about the increase in ill-trained laborers manning the historic fishing fleets of Puget Sound.

On page three were photos of several of the recent dead, including Danny. They used his yearbook shot. It showed a dark-haired, full-lipped, bored, and cocky adolescent with a face scarred by acne and a poorly tied tie. "Danny Jansen," read the caption, "had hopes of becoming a doctor."

No one at Golden Gardens had ever heard of this.

"Where do they *get* this shit?" said Brian. "A *doctor?*"

"A gynecologist maybe," said Steve.

"They just want to make it sound more tragic."

"It's not tragic enough?"

"Yeah, but they've got to make it more personal. Nobody knows who he is."

"*Was.*"

"Right. Fuck. Was."

Bert Jansen met the casket at Sea-Tac on a warm July morning. He followed the hearse to the funeral home over on the west side of Lake Union. He talked to Darla on the cell phone the entire way. She hadn't left the house, not once, since the news of the sinking had come almost two months before. In whispered, soothing sentences he assured her that traffic was fine, that they were making good time, that the black-suited staff was solemn and respectful.

When they arrived at the funeral home, after Danny's box had been unloaded and the cell phone tucked away, Bert caused something of a scene. He wanted to see the body. To be sure it was really Danny's. No, came the answer, gentle but firm. The identification was already positive, made from dental records faxed to the coroner in Anchorage. Besides which, he was told in lowered voices, there was nothing left, really, to identify. Nothing that looked remotely like Danny—or anyone else—anymore. It didn't matter, said Bert. He'd seen worse. Every damned day he saw worse: fires and car wrecks and his own share of drownings. Good God in heaven, did they think he'd never laid eyes on a drowned man? No, no, came the answer again—more firmly now, for were he really to insist there would be no denying him. No, he hadn't seen worse. This was his son. There was no worse.

Finally he relented, after much shouting and shushing in the mahogany-paneled office, and finally he finished up the funeral plans and walked out across the hot black asphalt to his car. He drove to a lounge he knew of near the docks, the back-back room of a terrible Chinese restaurant, where off-duty cops drank at odd hours. He put away two double bourbons at the mirrored bar and agreed with the bartender, whom he didn't know from Adam, that it was shaping up to be a fine day indeed. Then he drove home in the sunshine. On the way he called Darla and told her that everything had gone well enough, considering.

The Danny Bench was his idea. There was a place he had in mind for it, at Golden Gardens, the park by the marina, the one that Danny liked to go to with his friends. He'd been there a couple of months before, when he went to photograph the victim of a late-night shooting, a Hispanic boy found in the pedestrian tunnel beneath the railroad tracks. Near the beach was a platform that had one bench already; a black, whale-shaped thing that Bert sat on for a while when his job was done. Darla agreed that the park would be the best place for a memorial, but she wasn't ready even yet to go about the business of admitting that her son had died. Bert said that he would take care of the details.

The bureaucrats in the Parks Department were happy to supply him with the name of the whale-bench maker—a shipbuilder in Ballard, they said, who had designed the piece for his father. Bert visited Eric at his shop. He didn't seem to Bert what a bench-artist ought to be. Instead of a sensitive craftsman in a cluttered studio, Bert found a giant of a workman in a clean, if run-down, shop, behind which lay a yard cluttered with boats and hulls and inscrutable nautical whatnot. The only "art" visible was the Mount Rainier calendar over the desk in the office.

"I understand you make benches," Bert said.

Eric squinted for a moment with apparent disbelief, as though Bert had asked about sliced lunch meats or women's underwear—though he'd called just that morning to explain what he was after.

"I made one," he finally answered.

"The whale?"

Eric nodded silently. He held a tool in one hand, something like a long screwdriver, but with a head more twisted and complex.

"It's a beautiful piece of work," said Bert.

"Thank you."

Eric tapped the tool impatiently against his leg. Bert wasn't sure how to proceed.

"It was for your father?" he ventured.

Eric squinted again. "Did you know him?" he asked.

"No. They told me at the Parks Department."

Eric didn't say anything. He seemed to be waiting for Bert to get to the point.

"How did he die?" Even as he heard his own words, Bert couldn't imagine what he was thinking, asking such a thing. This wasn't his business—it had nothing to do with his visit. But he suddenly wanted to know.

Eric didn't seem at all bothered by the question.

"He was a fisherman," he said.

Bert felt himself go cold all over in a sudden rush of sympathy and kinship, and a sense of creepy inevitability. A fisherman, of course. Like Danny. He struggled to keep his voice level.

"I'd like you to make another one. Just the same. It's for my son."

Eric nodded again, but this time with more satisfaction.

"I kept the mold," he said. "But it won't be cheap."

V

Gerta took to walking the beach. Of course she went to Golden Gardens. She would hike a while in the wet sand, her flat canvas shoes tucked into the shoulder bag she used these days as a purse. Then she'd rest and watch the sea. Usually she sat on Shorty's bench, though sometimes she'd find a smooth log in a driftwood pile up the beach and sit on it, so that she could admire the bench as a stranger might. Every once in a while she strolled the marina end of the park and avoided the bench all together.

She visited in the early morning, before most of the work world was stirring. It was a time when the shore birds were apt to be

swimming fearlessly, close enough to tell the scaups from the sco-
ters, even with her old eyes. She liked the place best in these hours,
before the day's heat brought out either the bugs or the moms with
their toddlers; a time when she could think her thoughts without
interruption.

On days that were especially fine she might stay for several hours.
Later in the morning she often came across a ragged group of "no
goods," as Shorty might have called them—young boys barely out of
high school, up to nothing in particular, keeping their precarious balance on the edge of actual trouble. Vivian Bulberg had warned her
about them, calling them "gangs," but they hardly looked like what
you read about in the papers. Dr. Lauber reprimanded Gerta for walking
the park alone. He offered to accompany her, but Gerta said no. They
were just boys, after all; boys who weren't quite ready, for whatever
reasons, to be men. She'd watched them once, leaping and shouting
as a freight train rattled by on the bluff, acting for all the world like a
bunch of six year olds. They were nothing to be afraid of.

Sometimes she would see them sitting on and around Shorty's bench.
That didn't bother her either. There was nothing they could do to
hurt it. Except for somebody taking a chainsaw to it, Eric had said,
the bench was pretty much vandal proof. Gerta watched the boys
from afar, waiting for them to move on. Maybe if they sat long enough,
she joked to herself, something of Shorty would rub off on them.

She wondered what that might be. Something of impatience and
adventure? Of purpose and perseverance? Of duty? Or were these
even kin to the notions that had driven the man? It was hard to say. As
well as she ought to have known him, it was simply hard to say. So
much of his life he had spent at sea. What was it like, day after night
after day, to awake from damp, fitful sleep and to be greeted by nothing more tender than shrieking winds and pounding waves? What
was it like when the worst of the storms hit hard?

Early on Shorty had tried to tell her: "All you can think about," he
said, "is land." Well, he'd gotten his land, and put the waves behind
him. And apparently he decided that wasn't what he really wanted,
after all. For in the wicked wink of time it took to pull a shortbread

pan from the oven, he'd opened his skull on a parking berm, without so much as a kiss goodbye. Who knew what went on in that old fisherman's head?

She watched the young men clowning and drinking near the water's edge. A tall kid with a shaved head and an earring ran to the bench and walked unsteadily along its arched, Orca back, his arms flung wide for balance. A skinny cigarette burned in one hand. He held it with his thumb and index finger, like a dart. Halfway across he toppled, giggling, into the sand. Young Shorties in the making? It hardly seemed so. At their age, Shorty was long since a grown-up already. He wore a stiff khaki uniform and shoes so shiny you could see the moon in them. You really could. He'd showed her once, when he was home on leave in Botkins.

Ah, he'd been a decent man, all things considered, and if he was a little hard to figure out—well, from what she'd heard a lot of fishermen were worse.

One morning in August she arrived at the park on the #48 bus, just after nine o'clock. The sun was long since up, and the only traces of fog were miles away, lingering low on the hills of the distant peninsula. Two ferries approached each other out in the deepest water. It looked as if they might collide, but of course they were many lengths apart. No other boats were visible. A couple of dog-walkers tugged their charges away from the water at the high-tide's hard-packed edge; otherwise the beach was deserted. She headed for Shorty's Bench.

From far down the shore she could see that something was amiss. She was dizzy for a moment, worried that her mind was going or her eyes were playing tricks. She stopped against a gnarly driftwood log, a mighty giant nearly half her height. Her hands rose to her chest.

There were two benches. Two identical benches where Shorty's bench should be. Two leaping whales, angled slightly toward each other on opposite sides of the platform; Shorty's looking just a few degrees south, as it always had been, and the intruder on the same slight angle to the north, but with the whale facing the same direction, so that they seemed to be breaching in a line, like whales on the open sea.

Gerta tried to think when she had last been to the park—a week, maybe; no, surely less, as recently as last Thursday it was, or maybe Wednesday. She'd ridden the bus down as usual, and had sat on Shorty's bench and watched a Cosco container ship ease its giant bulk toward the city. She remembered the unearthly size of it, its multicolored trailers stacked like children's blocks. She had sat on Shorty's bench and by God there'd been only one, and now there were two and Gerta didn't know why.

She approached the platform cautiously. Beneath the intruder was a plaque, identical to Shorty's but for the lettering of another man's name: *Danny Jansen.* There was writing below, also much like Shorty's: *Taken by the sea.* And there was something else, between the benches: another plaque—a small one, brass, hardly bigger than her hand. She had to stoop a bit to read it, and stooping wasn't something she did easily anymore.

Arching Orca Benches, it read in small letters, *crafted by Eric Einar Olsen, Ballard, Washington.* Beneath that was an even tinier inscription, something about Seattle Parks.

Gerta nearly fell, trying to stand. She staggered back to Shorty's bench and sat. Eric. He'd made another, and he hadn't told her. He'd made another, and they'd put his name on a plaque like he was dead, too, like Shorty and this taken-by-the-sea fellow who was suddenly Shorty's neighbor. He hadn't told, he hadn't asked, he hadn't said a word. She was mad enough to spit.

Someone was approaching, coming down the walkway from the upper lot. Whoever it was moved slowly, as if they weren't sure where they were going. Gerta plucked a hanky from her pocket and wiped at her eyes beneath her glasses. It was a woman in a gray sweatshirt and shorts. She'd gotten closer but was still taking her time. As quickly as she could, Gerta scrambled off the platform and back the way she'd come, along the water's edge. She had no heart for conversation. The tide was ebbing, and she walked the line of the wet footprints she'd made coming the other way. When she passed the big log where she'd rested, she glanced back. The sweat-shirt woman, now just a figure in the distance, had reached the platform and was sitting on the stranger's bench, staring at the sea

Gerta struggled, barefoot, up the hill toward the bus stop. She would deal with Eric later. Or perhaps she wouldn't bother. What difference would it make? There was no use trying to figure him out. He was clearly his father's son.

VI

It's time to go. Steve has made up his mind. His old girlfriend Becky has written him—well, not him, exactly, but she wrote his buddy Mark, who she was seeing after Steve broke off with her. Mark showed Brian the letter, from Montana. It was all about the scene she'd found, and the people she'd met, and how much better it was there than in Seattle. She didn't say why, exactly. Just that it was better.

Steve imagines himself on a horse, the day's work ending, the Big Sky sunset going down easy. Not that Becky's letter mentioned horses. Apparently she's working as a fry cook in Missoula, at a diner with a card room and strip club in the back. But Steve figures the horse will happen eventually. He doesn't have a plan yet; not like his mom and dad want him to have. He asked to borrow the 4x4 and they said no. He asked for the bus fare. No again. Not until he had a plan. He made up his mind to go anyway.

Brian says he'll go, too. He doesn't have an old girlfriend, or a letter, or a plan either. He just knows he can't spend one more summer barbecue with his dentist father ranting at the picnic table about gum disease.

"You bet," he tells Steve. "Just say when."

Steve says when. Thursday morning, he says. The train they call the "Bud twenty-seven." It's a name they made up for the diesel freighter that always seems to roar by just as somebody is headed off for the day's first six-pack. In fact the train has become a kind of signal for somebody to make a run, on foot or bike or skateboard, or by car if they're lucky, for the convenience store on Shilshole Avenue, where the fancy seafood restaurants are lined up side by side across the wide, black parking lots.

They pack some trail mix and some extra clothes and two bags of good weed in the knapsacks they used to use for their schoolbooks. They wait in the tall grass at the park's north end where the tracks make a long, slow curve. Brian rips the crotch out of his pants trying to hop the link-and-wire fence, but he doesn't break the skin, and Steve says they'll deal with it later. When the train is bearing down for sure they make themselves tiny in the bushes, emerging at Steve's small shout of *now*. They run alongside, just keeping up, feeling the dull heat and power of the engines, and the trembling ground beneath. Some of the box-car doors are partway open, as they'd hoped, but they're a lot higher than it seemed from a distance; it will take a jump to get on. And they'll have to do it soon, for the flat space on the right-of-way is sloping to a brambly slide about thirty yards ahead, and it would be a long drop to the beach below.

Steve goes first. He jumps, arms out to grab anything, and feels for a moment that he is flying and falling all at once, until his knees hit something hard and there is wood beneath his palms and he pushes hard with his arms, his momentum carrying him forward and over in a clumsy half-somersault; but it works, he's on board. Below him Brian runs furiously, his face red, his outstretched hand looking huge and desperate. Steve reaches, and pulls, and they are together.

"Fuckin' A," he shouts. "We did it."

His eyes burn in the wind. He holds onto the door with both hands. The ground races beneath them in a torrent of brown and green. Through the trees they see flashes of the bright blue Sound. Then the tracks turn, and there is nothing but trees.

Steve moves away from the door. It's too loud to talk. The percussion of wheels on the tracks beneath them sounds like a dozen crazy snare drums. Inside the boxcar the air smells nasty; he wonders what it held before it held them. He hopes it's traveling empty all the way to Montana. He hopes they don't get caught and tossed off in the middle of the Eastern Washington desert. And that the nights don't get too cold. And that they get there before their food runs out. Brian is studying the rip in his jeans—Steve hopes he isn't pissed. That he won't try to jump off at the first opportunity. He hopes it all works, this running away without a plan. Ah, fuck it, he thinks. What choice was there, really? What was there left to hold him? He sticks his legs out and stretches, tries to relax. The train seems to be picking up speed.

Me and my bear in 1972, both of us prescient and, as a result, gloomy. I imagine we're simply mourning the fact that in thirty years neither of us will have nearly so much hair.

Bruce Machart's fiction has appeared in *Story*, *Zoetrope*, *Five Points*, and elsewhere. A graduate of the MFA program at Ohio State University, he has since been awarded a Tennessee Williams Scholarship from the Sewanee Writers Conference, the Frank O'Connor Prize from *descant* magazine, and an Individual Artist's Grant from the Ohio Arts Council. Machart's first published story appeared in *Glimmer Train* in 1998.

AMONG THE LIVING
AMIDST THE TREES

Bruce Machart

Half past quitting time on Friday, a day we began by liquefying a family of possums in the debarker, and Garrett and me are driving the drive we drive five times a week. Route 96, from the paper mill in Silsbee, where we turn logs into loose-leaf, to Jasper, where we head home to shake the bark dust from our jeans and blow it from our noses and wash it from our hair before we take our women out for dancing and beer. Friday evening in the full steamy blaze of East Texas summer, and someone's gone and let those little lovebugs out from wherever it is they keep them holed up the rest of the year. Garrett's drinking a tallboy, working a toothpick around in his mouth and cursing the black mash of bug guts on his Silverado's windshield. He's scratching his wiry red sideburns like they're overrun with mites, glazing and smearing the front glass over again and again with the wiper/washers. "These sumbitches is freaks of nature," he says. "Fucking and flying what all at the same time."

"And dying," I say. Straight forward through the windshield I can't see a thing, not a bit of the road, but on either side the forest is wet and green and rustling with breeze. Garrett's leaning his head out the window now and then to get a better look at the road, cursing when he catches a bug in his teeth. I'm staring straight ahead into the aftermath of a bug orgy gone bad, and the whole time there's green streaking by in the corner of my eye—the trees, the undergrowth, a whole forest full of little live things waking up for the nightlife.

Bruce Machart

"Yessir," Garrett says. "Dying in mid-lay. Sounds good until you figure they probably don't even get their rocks off. They're probably just thinking those hold-on thoughts, you know, imagining about nuns or unpaid bills or a car crash, and then—Smack! Windshield. The great hereafter and beyond. All that shit."

"You think bugs even got rocks to get off?" I say.

Garrett takes his foot off the gas and shoots me a look like maybe I've slid over next to him on the bench seat and asked could I hold him awhile, then something outside catches his eye. "Well, whatever in blazing hell is wrong with the critters around here today?" he says, kicking hard on the brakes and sliding the truck to a stop on the gravel shoulder. "Possums all ground up like chili first thing in the morning. Fuck bugs. And now lookit," he says, tossing his empty back into the truck bed. "Lookit here at these dogs doing it human style."

And there they are, sure enough having canine relations right down in the ditch next to a rusty corrugated culvert, the one on top some sort of hound mix—part beagle, part blue tick, maybe—and so in need of a meal that from up on the highway he looks to be all rump and ribcage. His little bitch, she's missing an ear, and he's got her pinned down tight, her back against the far bank of the weed-choked ditch. The old boy, he's going at it in that churning-butter, dog-lay way. Even so, I can't help thinking there's a twinkle of something tender about these two, the way her front paws are wrapped up around the scruff of his collarless neck, the way he's intent on licking where her ear used to be all the while he has his way with her. And his way *is* a strange way, after all, for a dog. "They're doing it missionary," I say, and it seems silly to admit, but the whole thing slicks my guts with a kind of greasy, nervous guilt, the likes of which I haven't felt since my wife caught me playing my own fiddle in the shower one time last year. "Let's go," I say. "Give the old boy some privacy."

"Privacy?" Garrett says, fishing what's left of the six-pack from off the floorboards. "When you want privacy with Glenda, tell me something, you generally haul her out here to the side of the highway?"

Garrett's the kind of man who does more talking than thinking. Just this week, when one of these shirt-and-tie reporters who've come

122   *Glimmer Train Stories*

nosing around since the murder asked Garrett if he thought Jasper was a racist town, old Garrett looked into the camera and spit between his teeth. "Hell no," he said. "We done elected blue-gums both as mayor and sheriff. Now what's that tell you?" Even so, Garrett every now and again makes good plain sense, so as crossways as it seems to be sitting on the side of the highway watching these dogs ravage one another, I've got to give the man his due. I crumple my empty and crack open a new can.

"At-a-boy," says Garrett. "We ain't going nowhere. This is something you don't get to see but once, if ever, and we're gonna just sit right here and drink a cold beer and see it."

Afterward, on the way home, we decide we'd rather be drunk early than clean. We're halfway there as it is, and Conway Twitty's on the radio singing about whiskey and women and hasn't once yet mentioned a shower or soap, so there's maybe one of those subliminal messages working on account of that. Besides, the way all these reporters have been jammed into Slyder's Saloon since those sick bastards dragged Mr. Byrd down a rutted road until there wasn't anything left to drag, we figure we'd best get there early if we want a table level enough to set a longneck on. Instead of showering, once we clear the cloud of lovebugs we crank down the windows to let the wind blast the dust from our hair. Outside, the sun is just beginning to hunker its way west, setting the treetops ablaze in such a way that the whole sky goes over to a kind of deep and waxy pink lipstick color. Garrett guns the engine and we speed toward home, breathing deep through our noses and shaking our befuddled heads at what we've just seen. It's a yeast farmer's wet dream out, too. The kind of hot and juicy you ought to be able to bottle and sell in drugstores. With the windows down, the forest smells akin to what you might get if you boiled Pine-Sol on the stovetop while roasting a sack of rain-soaked soil in the oven.

When we cross Route 190, Garrett veers left onto Main and spits out the window. Traffic's as heavy as it gets in a small town. High-school kids with nowhere to be but on the streets, big sweating men trying to get home from work, all of it made worse by the news crews mulling around double-parked vans with their satellite antennas reaching up high as old pines, all of them just waiting for air time so they can send word to the world of what a backward and bloodthirsty bunch of hicks we all are.

"If I was that dog," Garrett says, "I'd a never let my lady know there was an alternative to the dogstyle. She's liable to get it in her head the old way's degrading or something, least if she's like Sandy she would. Hell, sometimes I get so tired of the same old thing I'd damn near do it on the side of the road just to spice things up, you know? Ten years of walking on that-time-of-the-month eggshells and what do I get? But you wouldn't know nothing about that, now would you, Mr. Newlywed. Your Glenda's a grinder, is she not?"

Now, maybe if someday we find ourselves making conversation somewhere in a locked-tight and soundproof and windowless room, and Garrett's tongue is tore clean out of his mouth and he's got both arms ground down to stumps so he can't write or do that sign language the deaf folks use, maybe then I'll tell him straight away that yes, he's absolutely right. A grinder, I'll say. No two ways about it. I'll tell him how matter-a-fact she *does* like to do it on the highway, preferably while I'm driving, and in the living room, with the lights on and the curtains thrown wide. In the ladies' room stall at Slyder's one Saturday night. I'll tell him about the rooftop, so help me God, when a new moon gave the night fully over to darkness and I arched myself beneath her, crawfishing my way backward, scooting up the shingled slope from eave to peak, all the while pressed between the hot sliding softness of my wife and the roof rash rising on my elbows and ass. I'll tell him about the shingle grit I'd picked grain by painful grain for a week from my skin.

Hell, put us in a room with no ears and I'll even embellish some things, but not now. Not here. In this little neck of the Big Thicket, words bounce around from tree to tree, house to house, and mouth to blathering mouth, so I don't say a thing. A year back, the night before Glenda and I got married, her daddy, Tricky, threw us a party at Slyder's, rented the whole place out. This was in the days before he found out about his cancer, before his black hair turned loose of its gray scalp, and when he pulled me a new Lone Star from the ice and twisted her open he put his big, thick-skinned hand on the back of my neck and told me to be careful where I let my mind wander, especially when Glenda wasn't around to keep it penned up. Glenda's mom, he told me, had run out on him because he one time *thought* about cheating. He said news—true or otherwise—travels that damn fast or faster here in Jasper. Said all he was doing was having a dirty daydream about the new drive-thru girl at the Cream Burger, and when he got home the old lady had cleared out. "And all I done," Tricky said, holding his beer bottle like a microphone, "was lean in a little when this gal handed me my lunch so I could see what she had working under her shirt."

That's just the way it is around here, so I don't tell Garrett a thing. I don't mention how in the early days, after I'd run into Glenda at the Easy Clean Laundromat she inherited from her grandma and we'd been out a time or two, she took to taunting me. About how one night, while we walked along Coon Creek out back of my place, she'd crouched behind a sweet gum tree and stepped out of her dress before wading through the tangle of shoreline shadows and into the water. "Come on," she said, working water with cupped hands over her moonlit skin. "Get in here. You aim to be a man tonight or not?"

Instead, I let Garrett drive and I drink what's left of my beer and I try not to think too much about Glenda, about how her skin shines even in the darkness, even beneath the water; about how Garrett's wife, Sandy, spends her lunch break away from the police-station filing room where she works and eats instead at the laundromat, where she fills my wife's head with the latest horror stories about the way James Byrd was killed, about the root-riddled road that ripped his body apart as he thrashed and slid, chained behind his murderers' truck; about how Mr. Byrd used to smile and whistle while washing his work clothes on Sunday nights; about how Glenda's started talking lately about going out to Huff Creek Road so she can see where it happened, so she can smother her imagination in the reality of it, no matter how gruesome; about how tore up she gets nights on account of her daddy and his cancer; about how some nights she lets loose to crying even while we're making love, and how it hollows me out so that I think nothing will ever fill me up again.

Some nights I'll sleep in restless fits, the muscles of my lower back burning with spasms so that I dream I'm an animal with a boot on my neck and a red iron searing another man's initials into my hide. Every night this week, after I think she's cried herself to sleep, I've jerked awake to a bed half full and the sound of her voice in the hall. Even over the telephone, Tricky will have her in stitches, and through the cool hum of the air conditioner her quiet laughter will push its way into the room. I'll prop myself up in bed and feel the kinks in my back turn loose. And I'll listen, trying to imagine what he's saying, how he's managing to make her laugh.

"I can't push it out of my mind," Glenda will tell him. "I'm serious, Daddy. I keep seeing it. Over and over. His body tearing apart on that road, and it's not like I knew him that well, but I keep expecting him to walk into the store and set his laundry bag on one of the machines and nod and smile at me while he feeds dollars into the change machine. I keep hearing his whistling. He had such a pretty way of whistling, so high and sweet for a man his size, and he wasn't showy about it either. You could tell he wasn't doing it for anyone but himself."

And then she'll stop talking and start listening, her bare feet sliding across the hardwoods while she paces, her breathing loud enough to hear, and then she'll let loose the slightest of half-swallowed laughs. "It's just that I don't know what I'm ever going to do without you," she'll say, and I'll wonder how a man gets to be man enough to hear that and go on telling jokes. Man enough to give of himself exactly what's needed.

You aim to be a man tonight or not? It stings more than a little to think about it, but as Garrett pulls into the back lot behind Slyder's and tilts the rearview down so he can watch himself run a comb through his tangle of red curls, all I can think is that more and more, when I'm alone with my wife, it's not the wild sex I'm after. I don't want all the gymnastics or the risk of being seen or the shingle grit stuck in my skin. Instead I want her to laugh, to wink at me while stepping out of her skirt, to turn off the lights and shut the bedroom door and pull me with her beneath three or four quilts so that I can have her all to myself, so I can duck my head beneath the covers before we make love and see her skin glowing there in the darkness, calling to me in some shiny new language only I can understand, lighting my way while I reach out and hold her and keep her from crying and answer her in the voice of the man I've somehow managed to become.

Inside, standing back of the bar, Stu Slyder is damn near salivating at all the business coming his way on account of this murder. If you'd lived here all your life like I have, and you happened upon Slyder's tonight, aiming to have a long sit-down with the boys over a few cold ones, you'd no doubt stop at the door and marvel awhile, wondering if you'd taken a wrong turn somewhere, maybe stumbled across some secret white-collar society in your yellow-dog town. There are guys in neckties everywhere. Back at the pool table. Bellied up to the bar. And instead of the familiar stink—sawdust and sweat and spilled tap beer—the place is ripe with the smell of aftershave. Stu is smiling his gap-toothed smile, trying to keep his shirt tucked in despite the downward slump of his belly. He's sliding bottles across the bar, slicking the stray hairs of his comb-over back with the palm of his hand. It don't take much of a man, I'm thinking, to get rich off his hometown's troubles.

Garrett makes his way back from the bar and hands me a longneck. "Lookit that leech," he says. "Teeth on him, he could eat corn on the cob through a picket fence, and *would* too if he thought he could make a buck doing it. Promise him ten dollars for the pleasure and he'd kiss your ass on the steps of city hall and give you an hour to draw a crowd."

"He counts all his money after tonight," I say, "the price is liable to go up."

"Sounds about right," he says. "He's a counter, sure enough. Always did like that math. Sucked up to Mrs. Earlich so bad in algebra class you'd have thought her big tits reached out all the way to his desk."

Looks of Stu's new brick house up on the highway, I'm thinking, maybe we all should have sucked a little of that tit. He's a tight-ass, all right, but he ain't stupid. Besides, this is the only bar in town with a dance floor. And they still got Bob Wills on the jukebox. And then there's Glenda's daddy, Tricky, huddled as per usual around the big corner table with his fellow pipefitters playing forty-two, every one of their heads sheared clean as summertime sheep. They're slapping dominoes on the tabletop and scratching the backs of their necks and no doubt comparing notes on the Harleys they've got ready to roll out back. Six months back, after Tricky's first couple chemo sessions, all the boys of the pipefitters' local shaved their heads. It was a hard man's brand of brotherhood, and the night they did it Tricky walked into the bar, and when he saw them his eyes filled with a liquid look of something like love. These are rough-hewn and heavy men, men with calluses thick as rawhide, men who aren't afraid to keep something tender beneath their ribcages, and to expose it to the elements when occasion calls for it, no matter how it hurts. Tonight, it's these men and their laughter and the cold bite of beer on my teeth that set me at ease, despite the fact that Stu Slyder is talking quiet-like to one of these hair-gelled reporters, leaning in close enough to kiss the guy. He reaches across the bar and takes a sharply creased greenback from the man, some high denomination, I'm guessing, and I catch Garrett's eye and nod in that direction.

"A value-added whore," Garrett says. "I shit you not. Put a quarter in his ear and his teeth fold back."

"Save us some seats over by Tricky," I say. "I'll call the girls."

Garrett nods and I make my way to the pay phone in the back near the ladies room. As soon as Glenda picks up the phone she says, "Where are you and why aren't you here?"

"Got sidetracked," I say. "We hit some gravel on the way home, started sliding and slid clean over to Slyder's. Go get Sandy and meet us here, would you?"

"Figured as much," she says. "Already got the quilt in the truck, so don't get too drunk on me. I got plans for you yet tonight."

"Looks of this place," I tell her, "the whole world's got plans tonight, and they mostly include Slyder's. You wouldn't believe the out-of-towners."

"Well hang in there, old timer. I'm on my way. Is Daddy there?"

"Him and the whole crew."

"Well then it can't be *that* bad. They'd just as soon drink water as mingle with strangers."

"Then keep your headlights on bright when you pass over Coon Creek and you oughtta see them all bending down for a drink. I'm serious, sugar. I ain't ever seen the likes of this. I keep thinking of what my cousin Ty said after that school bus went into the ravine last year out his way and all those kids drowned. He likened living in Harlingen that week to being in the freaking zoo, and on the wrong side of the bars, too. Strangers gawking at you, getting on the TV and twisting things all around."

"Now hold on, baby doll," Glenda says. "I'm coming. If something's going to get twisted tonight, it better be me around you."

Back at the table, Garrett's holding forth with Tricky and the boys, throwing his hands around like he's on a Sunday morning church show and something holy's taken hold of him. I grab a couple new beers from the bar, and when I sit down he winks at me, popping a toothpick into his mouth. Next to Tricky are the Hooper twins, DJ and Teke, and their cousin Nelson, three massive men with shining scalps. You put this foursome in the bed of a pickup, the bumper would throw sparks going down the road. Now Garrett works his toothpick around in his molars awhile, then he plucks it from his mouth and points it at me. "So then the foreman, old Henderson, he tells us to fire up the debarking drum, and it ain't but seven-thirty and already it's hot as the devil's dick out, and let me tell you something about your son-in-law here, Tricky. He reckons he'll stand right in front of the debarker's vents while I run the first load of logs, figures he'll get a blast of fresh sappy air in his hair when I hit the pneumatics. So I crank that big bastard up and load it with pine and tumble them logs barkless and clean, real quick work, but when I release the valves and the vents spring open, all I hear is this poor boy cussing and carrying on. I mean, he's howling, so I shut the machine down and haul ass around to him thinking something's gone wrong, maybe he's hurt, and there he is, bloody as a blind butcher. Shit's in his eyes. He's spitting it out his mouth. And then it hits me. It's them possums again. We've caught them nesting time to time in the debarker drum when the heat gets bad. And I shit you not, we must've tore a half dozen or more of them little sumbitches to shreds."

Garrett stops now for effect while the boys start chuckling, looking at me sidelong, then he tilts his beer back and slams it empty on the table. Even I can't help but smile. "Yessir," he says. "Tricky, your boy here was wearing possum insides *all over* his outsides."

It's when the women show up that things begin to get ugly, but not on account of them. Sandy, she's decked out with that black hair pulled back tight as the skirt that's riding up on those wide, hand-hold hips. Garrett talks a lot of lonesome-man trash, but his woman's got on her the kind of gradeschool-teacher good looks that can drive a man to mischief when he's alone in the shower. As for Glenda, her hair's done up in pigtails. Her skin, it's got the sheen of something well-buttered to it, something so shining and bright you could kill the main to Slyder's breaker box out back and so long as she was there you'd still have enough light to drink by. They're lovely, the both of them, and they don't mind hearing it.

"There's my girl," Tricky says, pushing himself back from the table and slapping a palm against his knee. "Ain't she a peach?"

Glenda smiles, puts a hand on her hip and bats her eyes, then plops into his lap. "I'll bet you say that to all the girls who get your laundry done free for you."

"Sure do," he says, playing a domino from his hand. "Thing is, unless something's changed around here, and things rarely do, every girl who fits that bill has got her ass right this minute in my lap."

"How you feeling, Daddy? You know you're not supposed to be drinking a bunch of beer."

"Well it ain't going to kill me, now is it?" he says.

DJ and Teke raise eyebrows at each other and reach for their cigarettes. Nelson smooths a hand over his shaved scalp, says, "You're too damn stubborn to die, you old fart, so quit talking your sympathy talk and shake the dominoes. These women came to dance, no doubt, not to hear your bellyaching."

DJ and Teke nod and blow smoke from their noses. Garrett and me, we take the hint and haul our ladies to the dance floor, or what's left of it, given the crowd. Somebody's gone and paid a half dollar to hear Willie Nelson sing about blue eyes and rain showers and heartbreak, and when Glenda leans her head back into the crook of my elbow I can smell the honeysuckle lotion she smooths into her skin after showering. She tickles her fingers on the back of my neck while we turn and slide around the floor. On her face, wet-eyed worry.

"That Willie Nelson knows a thing or two," she says, closing her eyes.

"So do you," I whisper.

Six months back, when Tricky came straight from the doctor's on a Saturday afternoon to give us the bad news, Glenda and I were making love in the shower, and while we dance and Willie sings and Glenda leans forward, pressing her face to my chest, I'm in two places at once. My feet are sliding in time to the music, but my mind is under that spray of water with her, both of us lathered with soap, Glenda with a foot up on each side of the tub so she could bend her knees and lower herself down onto me while I blinked water from my eyes and held her hips, watching them fall and rise. "Every time we come here it's raining," she'd said, working herself against me. It's an old joke between us, one that deserved its silly little answer. "Every time it rains here we're coming," I told her. Then the door rattled and the muscles in Glenda's hips twitched and Tricky's voice was hot and thick as the bathroom steam. "You rabbits get on out of there," he said. "I've got something needs telling."

And now, as Willie winds it down and Garrett and Sandy dance over close to bump hips with us and laugh, Glenda lifts her face back from my chest and I see her dark eyes are drowning, and still she manages a smile. "I was thinking about your daddy catching us in the shower," I tell her.

She takes my hand and we stand there awhile, waiting for the next record to play. "I was thinking about Mr. Byrd," she says. "Sandy says they had to hunt with dogs for the missing pieces. Spent half a day drawing spray-paint circles on the ground where they found his dentures or keys, a hand with a ring still on its finger—like that. Can you imagine?"

"I can't," I say, sliding her into the first three steps of a waltz. I mean to say something else, but instead a hard little fist of muscles starts clinching down low in my back, and I'm listening to the whisk of our boots on the dance floor and holding my wife a little too tight for good dancing, and all I can think about is those dogs on the side of the highway, about how the one on top took the trouble to lick clean his little woman's wound, about how even animals find ways to be kind.

I loosen my grip on Glenda's hand and lead her into a spin. Her pigtails whip the air and the hem of her dress parachutes out and she lets loose of a little squeal. I reel her back in, stepping long on the hard note of the waltz as I pull her in tight. She slips her fingers into the back pocket of my jeans, and I'm about to tell her about the dogs, about how Garrett called their position human style, but that's when the music stops, and so do we.

We stop and turn and Stu Slyder is standing by the jukebox with the electrical cord in his hands. He's turning up the television set over the bar with the remote control. Up there on the screen is the slick-haired man I saw earlier pressing creased money into Stu's hand, and he's standing now in front of Slyder's, his lips curled up in such a way that folks in living rooms all over God's creation will know that it pains him just to be here, to be standing amidst our kind. This whole town stinks something fierce, he might as well be saying.

"Turn that mess off," Garrett hollers, but Stu's not having any of it.

"Fixing to be Candid Camera," he says, "so ya'll be on your best behavior."

On the television, the reporter is gesturing wildly, talking about the town and the men who'd spent many of their adult years in prison. "For all we know, the murder could have been planned in this very bar," he tells us. "This is where the suspects were arrested. Just out back of where I stand right now, in the parking lot, police tell us that the blood-spattered chain they allegedly used to drag the victim to his death was recovered from the bed of the suspects' truck."

Glenda steps close behind me, reaching her arms around my waist. Stu Slyder is taking baby steps toward the television set, beaming at this windfall of publicity. The bar, loud and alive with talk and music a minute ago, is now taken with the kind of quiet you mostly hear in churches or hospitals.

"Channel 3 News has since learned that the blood found on the chain and on one of the suspect's shoes matches the type of the victim, James Byrd Jr., and we have reports that other members of the upstart Aryan group have been known to frequent this establishment."

"What a bunch of horse shit," Garrett says.

Then the reporter opens the door and we begin to see ourselves on the television screen. I stand there stunned, my toes gone numb in my boots while the camera pans around the room and there I am, wide eyes rimmed in red, my work shirt faded and frayed near the embroidered nametag. Glenda's visible only as arms wrapped around my waist, and then we're gone, off screen, just like that, and I see what the reporter wants the world see, a table full of hulking, hard-looking men with shaved heads and lit cigarettes, dominoes standing in rows before them. Tricky and Nelson and the Hooper twins, they sit there fixed in the lights of the camera while this reporter talks about the Aryan Nation and the KKK and skinheads, and when Glenda pushes me out of her way and stomps over to the camera, for a moment I watch her, the real her, and then I turn back to the television and see her there, her pigtails bobbing behind her as she spits at the reporter and swings around to point a finger at the camera man, and at me— at all of us glued to the screen.

"They ain't skinheads, you asshole!" she screams. I'm right there, not ten feet from her, but what I feel instead of pride or love or some impulse to protect her is an acid-hot drip in my guts, a kind of embarrassment you feel for people you don't know when they come unglued on afternoon talk shows. "That's my daddy," Glenda says, and then she's flailing away at the camera and Tricky is up in a hurry, wrapping her in his big sunburned arms, and I just stand there, the only one left watching the screen, marveling at the television version of my life.

It's not until Stu Slyder steps in that I snap out of it. He's up there on-screen, his fat blue tongue visible through the gap in his teeth as he moves between the camera crew and Glenda, as he stutters and sputters and rants about the First Amendment and then—never mind that Tricky's got her in his arms, never mind that it's all under control—then the fat bastard leans in with two rigid fingers and thumps Glenda up high on the chest, just below the tender skin of her neck, and that's all it takes.

I haven't hit anyone since high school, haven't been hit since my father one time backhanded me in the jaw for getting smart with him about something I can't even remember anymore. But tonight it comes so natural I would swear it's something you're born with, the backward snap of the elbow, the instinctive grip of the other man's collar. The spill of adrenaline into your veins when you make blood spray from another man's nose. My knuckles crack with the impact, and the sound of it is sharp as the fireside pop of hickory kindling, only louder. His head, it snaps back and I jump him, slamming him to the floor. He's on his back, pinned down with that ridiculous flap of comb-over hair dangling around his ear, and I keep throwing punches, knocking his big head against the hardwoods with each blow until his eyes glaze over with a bloodshot brand of fear I've never seen before.

Then he kicks his legs hard and throws all his weight to one side and I'm caught for a moment off balance, reaching down to catch myself when he throws himself forward, slamming his forehead into my mouth, and I don't know if the cameras are still rolling or not, don't know if Glenda is burrowing her face into Tricky's chest or staring down at me with the same kind of unease I'd felt for her not a minute before. All I know is that my eyes are awash with hot white light, and that I've got blood in my mouth for the second time in a single day, and that mine tastes sharply of iron, and that Garrett is leaning down and hoisting me up by my belt saying, *Holy shit, Hoss, that was a serious big can of whup-ass,* and that when my vision comes back the first thing I see is the reporter with his microphone at his side and his eyes on the floor, probably praying I'm done swinging for the night.

Then we're making a break for it, shuffling past the pay phone for the back door, getting the hell out of there. In the parking lot, the moon is throwing light off the chrome of the pipefitters' Harleys as they kick them to life. Garrett's laughing hard, howling into the night, asking, *When did you get to be such a shit kicker?* as he loads Sandy into his truck and cranks it up. Glenda shoots me a long and blinking and altogether confused look, a look you might give your husband if, say, you caught him jerking off in the shower, then she climbs up into the driver's seat of my truck and slams the door. I circle around to the passenger side, breathing in the exhaust of all these loud engines, and before I get in I spit a fat wad of blood into the parking-lot gravel, and there, at my feet, half a tooth floats yellow and broken in a thick pool of red.

In the truck, I don't know what to expect. A stern talking-to, maybe. A ride home and a night spent alone in bed while Glenda walks the halls talking quietly into the telephone. Instead, there's an unexpectedly cool swirl of air pouring in through the windows and, outside, a drift of clouds running up on the moon. There's the hum of tires on concrete and the rumble of the engine through residential back roads to the outskirts of town, where Glenda steers over an old logging bridge and puts the headlights on bright and slows to a crawl, centering the truck on the dirt road while we bounce in and out of ruts and over roots and the chassis squeaks and shimmies. "Not afraid of ghosts," Glenda says, "are you, sugar?"

I inhale and the night air saws away at the exposed nerves of my tooth. Tree branches lean in to brush the truck's front quarter panels. Glenda, she keeps on driving.

"Don't know," I say. "Never met one."

A mile or so up, the road is roped off with yellow police tape. Glenda kills the engine and grabs the flashlight from beneath the seat. "Night like tonight," she says, "can't get any weirder, I'm thinking."

I climb down from the truck and duck under the tape, following my wife as she pans the flashlight beam from one side of the road to the other. All around us there's the clatter of falling branches and the hissing of the breeze and the frogs speaking up from the trees. The road falls off on each side into ditches littered with weeds and debris, and I begin to wonder just how the hell you can drive a man into these woods and drag him from your truck, how you can cave his head in with the heel of your boot and then hold him down, your knee on the back of his neck, while your buddies hitch chains to his ankles. I'm wondering how you can stand over him—no matter what damn color he is, no matter what you believe—smoking a cigarette until he comes to and you see the fear widening in his eyes. I'm trying to imagine how it might have played out, how it all might have looked, but what I see instead are Stu Slyder's bloodshot eyes, and now I'm wondering just what the hell I'd been thinking back at the bar.

Up ahead, Glenda stops and squats over a red ring painted onto the hard-cooked dirt. "Dear God," she says, shining the light up the road. "Look at them all."

And there, by God, they are: dozens of them, some big enough to outline a trashcan lid, others so small you could cover them with a coffee cup, and no pattern or order to them whatsoever. We walk up the road and Glenda bounces the light around from red circle to red circle, and the moon stays back behind the clouds, and the forest seems rightfully alive and loud. And they just go on forever. I'm thinking you could pull me apart however you pleased and no matter how you tried you'd never end up with enough pieces to fill these rings. I'm thinking there's a lesson in that, a lesson I might could stand to learn, something about how there's always more to you than what you might think, but then Glenda bends down and traces a finger around one of the red circles and it's all I can do to stand there and watch her.

"He could whistle like you wouldn't believe," she says, "a not-a-care-in-the-world kind of whistle, the same way Daddy used to." She looks back at me with an arm outstretched, and when I go to her there's nothing left but to get down on my knees there beside her in the dirt and watch while she flattens out her hand and rubs this circle of paint into the earth. "Just whistling like that," she says, wiping her hand on my jeans, "ought to be enough to keep you alive."

On the walk back, Glenda turns the flashlight off. I freeze and look around long enough to see that I can't see a thing, so I bring her in tight, and I hold her there in the darkness, and when she leans her head back from me I get ready to walk. But then her lips are on me, and they're open, and my mouth is all of a sudden so full of her that it's like I'm being kissed all at once by everyone in my life who ever loved me in the least.

Back at the truck, Glenda throws a quilt down in the bed and we undress each other there in the dark before climbing in. It's habit, something I'm so accustomed to that I don't question it until we're wrapped up together with the quilt over our heads, until she pulls one of my legs up between her own and I can feel her there, the soft and swollen wetness of her. Her breath pushes hot against my chest and my tooth is screaming, a sharp pain that burrows down through the meat of my gums and into my jaw, and I want like hell here to tell Glenda that we don't have to do this, that we can just lie here awhile and go to the house, that I understand what just happened out on this road. Truth is, though, that I can't put it into words, not just yet, and all I know is that her skin is so soft it pains me to even think about letting her go, and her breathing is steady and slow, the breath of the deeply dreaming, and I'm thinking she might sleep through the night for the first time all week. Still I can sense that she's waiting, waiting for me to say something, so I tell her the first thing that comes to my muddied mind. "Garrett and me," I tell her. "We saw a couple dogs today. Up on Route 96. Doing it missionary."

She rolls back, pulling me up onto her. She presses her mouth against my cheek and I can feel her smiling there in the dark. She whispers, "You did not," and slips me inside.

I close my eyes, swallowing hard as I push myself into her. "Did too," I say, and then we're wrapped up in warmth, wrapped up in each other and in the sounds of the forest around us, the wind and the trees and the insects almost mechanically loud, like they've been working all night to find the right riff, and with a little work I hear them not as a whole but as single instruments, the same way you can when you focus in to find the bass line as you step onto the dance floor, so your feet know whether to polka or two-step or waltz, except something's not right. Here I am, a man making slow love to his wife in the back of a pickup truck not half a mile from where another man was just this week murdered, and the forest has something too deep to its melody, something too low-down and rumbling. Despite the quilt over our heads, it's all of a sudden a slightly brighter night, and I'm sure, right up until the voice bounces around in the trees, that the moon's found its way out of the clouds.

But then it comes, my name called out like it's a question all in itself, and for the second time tonight I'm thinking about how Tricky caught us in the shower, only this time I'm not remembering it so fondly. This time I'm feeling again the hot flush of my ears and the nervous twitching in Glenda's hips, the way time stops for just a sliver of a second when two grown people who love each other freeze in the middle of their most private moment and hope like hell they're both hearing things. It's settling into me the way grit can settle into a man's skin that headlights don't feel the same as moonlight, and then I hear it again.

"Hey, bud," Garrett says. "You in there?"

I duck out from the covers, throwing the quilt over Glenda, and when she pokes her head out her pigtails are frazzled with static. She looks like a schoolgirl who's been caught by her daddy doing back-seat, midnight things, and I feel something warm and altogether newly formed ballooning wide in my chest. "Nice timing," I say, and Garrett comes over, his truck's headlights throwing his long shadow over us as he walks our way, scratching a toothpick around in his sideburns.

"Hell, you two," he says, "ain't enough *ever* enough?"

Glenda smiles without showing teeth, and I can tell she's not embarrassed. I can tell she's flattered, flattered to be young and wild and lovely enough yet to make even the likes of Garrett shake his head with envy.

Now the moon really does come skulking out from the clouds, and when my tooth throbs I realize I'm smiling. Glenda's toes are curling around in my leg hairs, telling a little joke of their own, and when I look over her lips are pressed into a girlish grin and it's clear that she's more than happy to let me do the talking.

When I look back at Garrett he's shuffling his boots in the dirt. His eyes shift quick from Glenda to the ground.

"Out looking for more dogs to gawk at?" I ask.

"I wish," he says.

"What, then? They looking for me back in town?"

"They are," he says, and then he turns to Glenda. "They already came by our place. Sandy said you had some wild idea about coming out here and having a look."

"She's got lots of wild ideas," I tell him, but Garrett just rolls his eyes and keeps talking. Old Stu's hot, he's saying, wanting to press charges, wanting some payback. "I dropped Sandy at the police station on the way. She thinks maybe she can talk Sheriff Duecker into cutting you some slack, but all the same I wanted to warn you. You'd be in a fast river of shit if they found you out here."

"They bothered Tricky and them yet?"

"I doubt it. They tore off toward the highway when we ditched the bar. They're probably bellied up to another game of forty-two down in Kirbyville by now."

"Well, hell," I tell him, standing up in the bed of the truck. "I better get on into town then and turn myself in before they get back. Last thing Tricky needs is to come home to cops at his door and people talking all over town about his son-in-law the fugitive."

Glenda leans back against the cab and shakes her head. Her eyes water and sparkle in such a way that I know she's trying hard not to laugh. "I don't guess they'll need to frisk you," she says, and I look down at myself, a man with flecks of sawdust in his chest hair, a man wearing nothing but moonlight and pale skin and not-so-white socks. A man I don't yet fully recognize.

"I hate to do it, Glenda," Garrett says, "but I'm going to turn my back now so you can get dressed." And then he does; he turns and walks away and waits with his back turned, leaning on the door of his truck while Glenda fishes around in the quilts and hands me my jeans. I stand there awhile before putting them on, and I wink at my wife, and I look out into the forest where the crickets and frogs are still carrying on.

"You gonna bail me out?" I ask, and Glenda grins as I step into my pants. She stands, letting the quilt fall away from her. "I believe I will," she says, and I nod and smile and buckle my belt, and her skin is shining so bright and warm it's a wonder I don't melt.

INTERVIEW WITH MARY GORDON

by Charlotte Templin

Photo credit: Joyce Ravid

Mary Gordon

Mary Gordon has been a greatly admired novelist since the popular and critical success of her first novel, Final Payments, *in 1978. She has continued to win the attention and respect of critics and the gratitude of an appreciative public with subsequent books. She is the author of five novels, three novellas, a volume of short stories, a book of essays, two memoirs, and a biography of Joan of Arc.*

Gordon is the Millicent C. McIntosh Professor of Writing at Barnard College and also teaches at the Columbia University Graduate School of the Arts. Her awards include the Janet Heidinger Kafka Prize for the best novel written by an American woman for Final Payments, *the same award for* The Company of Women, *the New York Public Library's Literary Lion award, the Lila Wallace–Reader's Digest Award, and a Guggenheim Fellowship. A lifelong New Yorker, she lives near Columbia University.*

One of the central preoccupations of Gordon's fiction is the subject of the good person, something that came up in our conversation. We talked about Irish Americans and Irish-American literature, Gordon's journey in fiction writing, and her thoughts about her relation to writers of the past, and importantly, Gordon's memoirs: The Shadow Man: A Daughter's Search for Her Father *and* Seeing through Places: A Reflection on Geography and Identity.

Can we talk about interviews for a moment? Do you get tired of giving interviews? Or do you think about the possible benefits—that an interview may get you new readers?

The interviews one does on tour can be just mind numbing, but what I feel is that I am always very moved when somebody has read my work carefully, and often an interviewer like you has given me the kind of attention that I can only be grateful for. So I hope that the interview will get me new readers or readers of a different depth.

You mention that after writing the memoir about your father [The Shadow Man]*, you suffered a loss of faith in memory. That seems like a grave loss.*

It is a grave loss, but it's the loss of a romance. Virginia Woolf said that what you are trying to do in writing is to tell the truth and create something of beauty. If as a writer what you are doing has any moral significance at all, you are looking for the truth. If memory is a distortion or a work of fiction, you have to witness that. Even if it's painful, it's your job. That's just the way it is. And there is a kind of exultation that comes with the truth telling.

I felt that exultation in the truth telling about your father in the midst of the pain.

You don't have to be afraid of that ghost popping out of the closet any more because you have confronted the ghost. He can't surprise you; you don't have to be worried about ambush, and that's a liberation.

Memoir writers have to be willing to tell secrets. Do memoirists worry about that? Do they think about specific readers?

For me I would feel that I had the right to tell my own secrets. But if I really felt that somebody else's secret was very important to their sense of themselves, I wouldn't feel it would be my right to tell that. Everybody whose secrets I told is dead. I do feel that people have the right to their own secrets, and I don't believe in outing. Were my mother not in the cloud-cuckoo-land of dementia so she couldn't be hurt by it, I wouldn't feel that I could write to tell her secrets. I remember a letter of Elizabeth Bishop to Robert Lowell. She criticized him for using some of her letters, which she thought he had no right to publish. She said to him, "Art is not more important than everything." I'm on Elizabeth Bishop's side.

Is memoir still as popular a genre as it was at one time?

I think that people are beginning to feel that everybody on earth has now written a memoir, so perhaps it's a little bit less fresh.

I think it was Annie Dillard who said that one challenge for the memoirist is deciding what to put in and what to leave out.

Yes, and in that it's not unlike the shaping of fiction. In the end there is a form; there is a shapeliness that makes demands, and it's really a formal or almost a rhythmic question.

Would you extend that at all? Is memoir writing not that much different from fiction writing?

It is and it isn't. There are some things, which, if left out, would make an untruthful record. Memoir has a responsibility to truth or the truth as best as you can tell it. That is to say, if you willfully suppressed something—well, there is no point writing a memoir if you don't want to tell the truth as you see it. To deliberately fudge something that made you look better, or made someone else look better—that's the kind of issue that comes up in memoir that does not come up in fiction. In fiction it doesn't matter if you want to make the character look better or worse; you do that.

One of my students was telling me about a memoir by Toscanini that was distorted to enhance the image of the writer.

I have a lot of trouble with Lillian Hellman. The books work very well as literature, but they are morally flawed. There are moral issues in memoir that don't come up in fiction.

Pentimento is a wonderful book.

It is wonderful, but it's quite untrue.

William Zinsser said one writes memoir to justify one's life—to oneself, presumably.

I think that is very true. I think that if you're a writer, you only believe you've got something right if you wrote it down. and I think it's a way of checking if you have understood yourself correctly.

Your most recent memoir, Seeing Through Places, *is organized around places. Did that organizing principle came rather easily?*

I just began writing about place because I'm interested in writing about place, and then I said, "Oh, my goodness, I have quite a few of these. Maybe if I put a few more in that will work." I can't praise myself and say I thought it up. It came to me.

And what about the shaping of the book into a kind of journey?

It just seemed to come. Because of my belief that place gives us a lot of information about ourselves that we can't always get to directly. Memory releases information.

So place is one genesis of writing for you?

A lot of the writing that I love very much has a very strong sense of place, however you define place—as landscape, terrain, house, room. You have to inhabit a space. That relationship between the inhabiter and what is inhabited can be a very fruitful one. And the kind of fiction that I don't like doesn't have much sense of place. It all seems to take place in someone's head.

Can you give some examples?

I'm not a great fan of extremely self-referential fiction. Somebody like Calvino doesn't do it for me, or Borges. Donald Barthelme doesn't. And a lot of the metafiction, whose subject is fiction.

In Seeing Through Places *you describe not just your grandmother's house, but that house as connected with a way of life.*

One of the things that I do with my fiction students is to get them to try to consider that every family has a way of doing things. Then you bring your friend home from college and they say, "Why do you put the kleenex in the piano bench." You say, "Everybody puts the kleenex in the piano bench." Your friend says, "No, they don't." So I think all families have odd ways of doing things that are considered very normal in the family or else are just puzzles that you can imagine have the inexplicability of the holy trinity. But I think that's an interesting way of looking at the family. You know how they inhabit oddly without realizing that it is odd. For example, in my grandmother's house, why did my uncle sleep on the porch? There were two spare bedrooms upstairs.

You have written your father's story before The Shadow Man—*as a young girl you wrote his life as a saint's life; as a fiction writer you used him as a model for some characters—can one use the term model?*

A presence.

Is it appropriate to call him a muse?

Yes, that's an interesting way of thinking of it. I never have, but that's wonderful. He's my muse and the angel on my shoulder. The thing about my father was whatever I did he felt was fantastic. I think that's what every writer needs—some angel saying, "You're great, you're great, you're great!" twenty-four hours a day. Because there's also the devil on your shoulder telling you that you are completely worthless and your enterprise is delusional.

I was really impressed by your commitment to finding out the truth in The Shadow Man. *The detective-story aspect of the book is wonderful, but there was an element of luck involved, was there not?*

I don't know how it happened. I was giving a reading at Goucher College in Baltimore—not any place that had anything to do with my father—and a woman rabbi was in the audience. She said, "I know somebody who does Jewish genealogy in Cleveland."

That was where your father spent his boyhood.

How did she happen to be there? I just don't know. So that was a major piece of good luck. But then, when I got to the records of the nursing home in Cleveland—the poor house—where my grandmother died, and her file was missing, I just wanted to lie down on the library table and weep. Because those records could have provided all the pieces of the puzzle, like what happened to my grandfather. It could have explained why she was in the poor house when my father was working, and there was another daughter.

One would have expected her to be in the home of one or the other in that generation.

So the question was "Why?" I looked over the other applications, and one of the very interesting things I found was that one of the common reasons that old people got put into that home, which was a

Jewish home, was that they demanded keeping kosher, something the younger generation didn't want to do. So they would put particularly the mothers in the Jewish home rather than keeping kosher themselves. That was simply fascinating.

How did you explain that?

It was the story of the pressure of assimilation. To keep a kosher home would be to admit you were not assimilated. And pressure to assimilate was so enormous that they preferred to put their mothers in a home.

Choosing assimilation over the possible shame of putting one's mother in a home, not to mention the pain inflicted on one's parent?

Yes. It gives you a sense of what that pressure was. And one of the reasons I really wanted to test my father's story was that I got so damn sick of hearing how great immigrants did—what a wonderful experience. They all shaped up and assimilated. What's the matter with these people that want bilingual programs and want to define themselves ethnically. Why can't they be like our parents who just shut up and shaped up—and look how wonderfully they did. Well, not everybody did so wonderfully. And there were terrible, terrible psychic payments exacted. That was part of the story. My father's extreme pathology was part of the immigrant's story in America. I felt that it was not only my story or my father's story; it was an important part of the story of anti-Semitism in this country and in the world. It was an important and unique instance of Jewish self-hatred and of the distortions that caused.

The Shadow Man *ends up as a tribute to the Jewish people. It's about your embracing your Jewishness. At the end you have a lot of compassion for your father.*

I do. I think he was broken by anti-Semitism.

In the book you imagine how the world would have looked to him as a young man—pretty unwelcoming for a Jew. One gift your father gave you is the confidence and the desire to write.

Oh, yeah. There are things I am extremely grateful to my father for. Growing up as a girl in the fifties there were things you weren't supposed to do. Well, I never heard that. I never heard you are not supposed to be smart; you're not supposed to say what you think. You're not supposed to write. You're not supposed to spend your time reading.

You never heard it from him.

He was the most important person in my world. What the rest of the world said came into my one ear, but I felt like the real story was, "Of course you can do this." Anybody who didn't think so was not quite up to scratch, and I didn't have to pay any attention to them.

I remember reading about studies on the importance of a father's encouragement in women's achievements.

And something that makes me feel happy is a study that was done on judges who were very good on women's issues—divorce issues, rape. It turns out they had daughters.

Another interesting subject in The Shadow Man *is the search for the past—your reflections on people's pursuit of the past. You say we search out the past to "assure ourselves that we are not alone."*

The sense of being alone in the world makes people do extreme things. Post-enlightenment thought has not come to terms with that in our very proper exultation of the individual. Yes, it is very important to be an individual, but nobody wants to wake up in the morning feeling like they are alone in the universe. However we define connectedness, it is extremely important. I think it is one of the reasons why people join fundamentalist groups. They can make a connection very easily, very palpably with others who are like them and others who have gone before them and they get to say, "I am like you and I am not like you." That seems to be a very deep human need.

You also say that "what is unbearable is that the world went on before our births."

We don't like to believe that the world was there before we got there and will go on after we leave. There's a whole thing out there that we have no connection with.

It all happened and I was not there to see it—to be a part of it. So it is the job of the novelist to tell us about it—and also to tell us about the stories of the past that are not success stories.

You turn on your cable station, and an ad comes on inviting you to trace your genealogy. You don't want to hear that your great uncle was in jail. Everybody has a great uncle who was in jail, and a great aunt. People don't want to hear that. It would be so good for people to know everybody's history is a mess. I believe that would be immensely politically important. It's interesting that if you look at divorce statistics from the nineteenth century, they are very high, particularly among the pioneers. Marital instability was high. Guys were taking off all the time, and people don't know that. If you look at history you find alcoholism, desertion, abuse. There is this romance about some pristine family in the past that never existed. I think it is extremely politically dangerous. There is the idea in the minds of some people that everything was fine until all "these people" started complaining, and then the problems started. Those who caused the problems were people who said, "We are not trying to be you; we are trying to be ourselves." People just want to put everything back in the box. Of course, some things I believe are truly better now. People had lives of terrible shame and terrible lack of recourse. If you just think about the way we treat rape now. That's an enormous gain. Very, very few people would feel easy about publicly blaming a woman who was raped now. That's a step forward.

My students tend to believe the American Dream is there for everyone.

I guess they sort of have to, but there should not be shame attached to not succeeding. And there shouldn't be such a narrow definition of success. There shouldn't be a cover-up of the failures as if they didn't exist or it was their fault. Barbara Ehrenreich's book *Nickel and Dimed* is very good about how stacked the odds are against people.

You have a fascinating essay about Irish culture in Good Boys and Dead Girls, *in which you describe your relatives' negative reactions to your work. Were you surprised by that response?*

It was no surprise [laughs]. And that's why my background was so odd, because I had my father and this fantasy of Jewishness which valorized the life of the mind, and then these Irish people who said, "Stop dreaming, get your head out of the clouds." So I never imagined for one second that they would approve. Their response was no surprise to me. I separated myself from it. I did have this ferocious heat-seeking missile aspect to me—ready to go, to leave. It wasn't particularly hard because they weren't particularly nice.

I'm sure they loved you very much, but they thought of you as an outsider, I take it.

They didn't love me very much. My mother did.

They would have liked a little girl who was...

Obedient, practical, athletic, social. I understand why they didn't like me. I was sitting in a corner staring at them all. What's to like?

I read recently a remark by Walter Mondale about how he was shaped by his upbringing by Norwegian parents. He was not allowed to say anything that could be construed as bragging. Is that the sort of thing you are talking about?

Yes, but the Irish are tricky because the Norwegians are silent. The Irish talk a lot, but they don't tell you anything. So people think they are expressive people when they are not. Nobody thinks the Norwegians are expressive. One of the things that makes me laugh is people who go to Ireland for a couple of weeks, and come back saying, "Oh, we went to the pub and they told us everything." Aha! They told you nothing; they just talked a lot. A lot of Americans think they get Ireland when they don't. They get the story that is being packaged for tourists, which is a very charming story. It's self-protectiveness. They were colonized people.

So does the Irish character make the Irish good subjects for fiction?

The Irish are ridiculously over-represented in literature, but not Irish Americans. In America the Irish were introduced to American practicality and American ambitiousness. That's why we don't have a lot of Irish-American fiction. The Irish have faith in the invisible. They believe in poetry in a very strong way. Americans don't, so that I think the Irish who survived and prospered in America were the more practical.

And you've written about Irish-American immigrants in fiction.

In *The Other Side.*

You have suggested that there is a lack of an audience for Irish-American writing.

I think that the problem is that Irish Americans were compared with Jewish Americans, and there was a great audience for Jewish

American writing for two reasons: first, Jews are great people of the book, and so they were better educated. And second, after the Holocaust there was a curiosity about Jews. The Jew became something of an exotic, something we needed to know about. Similarly with blacks. There is no sense that we need to know about the Irish. They are not perceived to be doing anything to you, and also they weren't destroyed by Hitler.

And furthermore if they were assimilated…

Right, they are very easily assimilated in ways that blacks certainly aren't.

But it is important for us to remember the story of the first Irish. There was a lot of pain there.

And a lot of shame.

Then you also say the hiddenness of Irish lives make them good material for fiction.

It's a story that hasn't been told so much, so it makes a fresh story.

But you also write about German Jews and others. Do you choose other subjects that have hidden lives?

It seems to be the subject of the fiction writer. Wherever I find it I go after it. But it's not as if I go after things. To say "go after" suggests grand control and intentionality. They come to me.

One thing you are deeply concerned with in your writing is the question of what is a good person.

I have been tortured by the problem of goodness and also interested in how difficult it is to portray goodness in fiction. Everybody loves bad characters—Becky Sharp, Dostoevsky's characters. If one wants to live a moral life, fiction ought to be able to help us in deeper ways than the Victorians do—to really help us understand what goes into making a person of virtue.

That's very clear starting with your first novel, Final Payments.

What is genuine goodness, and what is self-hatred? I think there is such a thing as genuine goodness fueled neither by self-hatred nor shame. It seems to me that teasing those apart is a very interesting journey.

That comes out of your religious background.

As a person of faith, you have to think about being good.

The concept of the good person is a long-standing preoccupation in fiction. Among the Victorians, there's George Eliot.

I'm much more moved by the way George Eliot does it than by the way Dickens does it. I love Dickens's descriptions, and I think he is very good on eccentrics, but I don't think he is good on virtue in the way George Eliot is.

As Virginia Woolf says, Eliot is the only novelist who writes for adults.

What about Virginia Woolf?

She is very important to me. I started a doctoral dissertation on Virginia Woolf. I never finished it, but she was the person that turned me to prose writing.

Have you thought about the moral influence you might have?

I'll tell you my favorite story of the lack of moral influence I have. A long time ago a woman in my neighborhood would complain about what she called colored people. And I remember she once said, "That disgusting Geraldine Ferraro—anybody thinking that I would vote for a woman for vice-president, that's the most disgusting thing I ever heard!" And of course she had a Ronald Reagan button the size of a large pizza. Anyway, on another occasion, when she heard that I was the author of *Final Payments*, she said, "Oh, my God, *Final Payments* changed my life." So I thought what was she doing with *Final Payments*? How did it change her life? How could it change anybody's life?

To go back to the Victorians, people like George Eliot actually thought they could change people's lives.

Well, first of all they were working in the dominant medium for their time. There were, you know, crushes when the last serial parts of *The Old Curiosity Shop* would come to the docks. Nobody is going to kill anybody to get one of my novels. We're not the dominant medium; we are sort of flies on the screen of culture in terms of what really hits large numbers of people. Did Dickens and Eliot really change the way people thought? Probably the person who did the most was not a very good novelist—Harriet Beecher Stowe. I think *Uncle Tom's Cabin* probably did change things, but it's a lousy novel. And if you want to ask, "What changed more lives, *Uncle Tom's Cabin* or *Middle-march*?" it's *Uncle Tom's Cabin*. But which would you rather have written? So I think even the influence in the past is more about popular media than about art—and it's not gonna happen now.

Can you say something about the circumstances under which you got your first novel, Final Payments, *published?*

It's a very funny story, and it's not replicable. I was living in England, unhappily married to an Englishman. I was writing my dissertation on Virginia Woolf—in the British Museum every day. I was writing *Final Payments*. I was completely lonely and spending many hours a day crying. London is a hard town to crack. I'm from New York, and in New York you can go to the candy store and have a little banter with the candy-store owner. You get a cab, and you have a conversation. You buy vegetables and have another little riff. I was used to that kind of open joking around. In London I was not getting anywhere with the people who sold me milk or the people at the laundromat. It was making me cry, and I felt completely lonely. So I watched a TV show with Margaret Drabble, a writer I admired very much. I wrote her a letter telling her about my problems with the green grocer and the person who sold me milk, and she called me up and said, "We're not being very nice to you in London. Why don't you come and have dinner?" I wrote to her in care of the BBC. I had published nothing. I didn't know her. It was a complete fluke. She invited me over to dinner; she's the nicest woman in the world. I think she thought I was having a nervous breakdown. The other guest was a poet who *was* having a nervous breakdown. I spent the whole night listening to his nervous breakdown; I didn't say one word to Margaret Drabble. When I left, I was completely depressed: "You really blew it. You don't know how to take care of yourself. This was a contact. She's gonna think you're an idiot. She's gonna think you're the most boring person in the world, and she'll never get in touch with you again." She called me up and said, "You were so kind to my friend who was a poet and was suffering. And I'm so sorry that we didn't get to talk, so come and have lunch with me." We had lunch, and I gave her *Final Payments*. She read it, she loved it, she sent it to her agent. And that's how I got started. It is not a story that is a model for anything. It was complete chance.

Can we talk about your novel Spending? *How did the novel come about?*

All of my women friends have men in their lives—or partners—and a lot of us have children. But a lot of us get extremely impatient at our friends and colleagues who have servants that they happen to be married to, who just think it is an honor to serve the artist, and that is all they want to do. I'm not saying these women are being used; they often enjoy that. I think it's wonderful for them. All that I'm saying is why aren't there any men who want to do it? If it's such a great job, why don't men want to do it? We talk about this at great length. The novel started with a lot of my friends being "crabby" about why men don't think it's a wonderful honor for them to clear time and space for us. That was the source of the novel. After I wrote *The Shadow Man*, which was grueling emotionally, I thought it would be fun to do comedy. I looked at the dominant fiction, which had been written about women largely from a male perspective—if any women had good sex in literature, they always died, or their children died, or their children were horribly maimed, or they were horribly maimed, or their lover was maimed. There was a lot of maiming, corpses, bodies littered about. If you read much of the important literature of the West, you would think automatically if a woman had good sex, somebody was killed. I had in fact known some women who had good sex and lived, and I thought that should be witnessed in literature. So I thought it would be fun to write about it.

Most of what has been written about female sexuality by the great masculine writers has been what men want. It really is very different, what women write. I saw an exhibit of Pontormo drawings in London—I started looking at a lot of dead Christs, and I thought they looked spent, not dead. And I saw I could also talk about our relationship to the art of the past—those of us who love the art of the past never throw it out. We don't say, "Shakespeare has nothing to teach me; Tolstoy has nothing to teach me." I think among creative women who are writing now our relationship with the others who have gone before isn't adolescent rebellion, but it is a mature, "I'll listen to this, I won't listen to that."

What about your romance with painting?

I love painting, and I have less talent than anyone … And I tried, I took a drawing class and got better, but the starting point is so pathetic. I never really got to be the painter that I dreamed.

Can you talk about how you start a work?

I think I have an intense relationship with writers whose voices can be what I call a "tuning fork." There's a funny period before I really get started in a work—you know how dogs run in circles until they can figure out the exact spot where they need to lie down? I'm kind of like that until I can find the writer whose tone of voice really gets me going, and for each little project (a part of a book or a whole book or a story), I need almost to hear the tone in my ear. I have a very dependent relationship on the writers, but it's not like I'm going to copy them, or like I can't do something different from them. It's like having an older sister or brother start you on the road, because the road is dark, and you don't know where you are going. I feel like I have a very dependent—and mainly oral—relationship to the writers who have gone before.

How has your writing changed over the years?

I think I've gotten a lot more relaxed. I used to be really obsessed with a very, almost symmetrical, formal structure, and I was less willing to let the unconscious or associative patterns dominate form. I wanted to see a logical orderly progression in the way I structured things. I think I've been more willing as I've gone on to let myself be surprised, to let things like silence and uncertainty and self-referential discussion about the nature of writing come in and create forms that are a little bit more open.

Can you say something about your choice to focus on story? You said earlier that you are not a great fan of metafiction.

Story is one of the basic human impulses. Every child wants a story told to them; we all like to sit around the campfire and listen to stories. Non-narrative, really non-narrative fiction—a lot of post-modernist fiction that is so self-referential—is not of great interest to me. As human beings, we want to make contact, and the impulse to story is very great. Sometimes I feel dorky, like I'm not cool, which is painful. That's why it's very important to be rooted in other writers. You look at older writers and think, "What do I really want to do?" And doesn't that matter more than who's the queen of the prom, which *is* a strong impulse? I would like to be the queen of the prom, and I'm not gonna be the queen of the prom if I write the way I want to write, but I think self-referential, metafictional writing is a less human and less rich way to write. I've had to make a decision. If I'm gonna do it the way I do it, I'm gonna be considered a little retro and a little uncool.

Charlotte Templin is Professor of English at the University of Indianapolis. She is the author of *Feminism and the Politics of Literary Reputation: The Example of Erica Jong*. Her interviews with contemporary women writers have appeared in the *Missouri Review*, the *Indiana Review*, the *Boston Review*, and *Poets & Writers*.

This was me at the age of the narrator of the story:
hiding in my room, reading a book.

Ann Hood is the author of seven novels, including *Ruby* and *Somewhere Off the Coast of Maine*, and the non-fiction book *Do Not Go Gentle: My Search for Miracles in a Cynical Time.* "An Ornithologist's Guide to Life" is the title story of a collection to be published this year by Norton.

AN ORNITHOLOGIST'S
GUIDE TO LIFE

Ann Hood (signature)

Ann Hood

All of the houses on our street were in some form of disrepair. This was Park Slope, Brooklyn, 1974, the land of brownstones to be had for next to nothing. Crumbling, linoleumed, shag carpeted, knotty oak-paneled brownstones. They held the promise of hidden treasures in the form of parquet floors and intricately tiled fireplaces. At dinner parties, my parents and their friends talked endlessly about what they had uncovered. The spring the Bishops arrived, the biggest find belonged to the Markowitzes: an entire staircase, small and steep and painted sea green. We speculated about the slave trade, prostitution, homosexual love. But the Markowitzes only gloated, happy to unseat the Randalls, who had discovered an entire stained-glass window that winter. Cracked and missing pieces, it still stood as a majestic tribute to everyone's wisdom in leaving Manhattan with its crime and high rents and small apartments for Brooklyn, the New Frontier.

I was eleven going on twelve the year the Bishops moved across the street from us. I had bad tonsils. They had to come out. But every time my surgery date neared I got another bout of tonsillitis. By March I had missed fifty-two days of school and developed an allergy to penicillin. To keep me occupied—our family was in a no-television phase then—my father gave me a guidebook to birds and a pair of binoculars. "Open your eyes, Alice," he told me, "to the exciting world of ornithology." Then he went off to work.

The year before he had told me, "Everybody talks about the weather, Alice. But nobody does anything about it." For a while I measured rainfall and hours of sunlight and tracked the highest and lowest temperatures around the world. But then the tonsillitis began and I abandoned meteorology. Ornithology could be practiced from my bed, if necessary, though on good days I walked the four blocks to Prospect Park in hopes of an exciting discovery.

From my room, I could gaze out the bay window and into the treetops. Beyond the treetops I could see the Bishops' house, perfectly. Since the variety of birds in Brooklyn was small—sparrows, robins, and finches mostly—watching the Bishops was at least equally as interesting.

The day they moved in, a cold and rainy March day, I was home with a new bout of sore tonsils, eating blue popsicles and hoping for a cardinal sighting. Instead, I saw the U-Haul truck pull up and the Bishops emerge, blinking and dazed like they had landed on the moon. All of them looked misplaced, even the father, who lacked the efficient demeanor of most of the fathers I knew. Mr. Bishop appeared to have just woken up. Mrs. Bishop seemed about to break, too delicate and fragile for a mother. Normally I would have delighted in spying two girls moving into our neighborhood, but these two, shivering in their thin cotton shirts and jeans jackets, wispy blonde hair tangling in the rain, did not look like new friends to me.

Just-beginning-to-bud trees blocked the view between the street and the Bishops' third floor. Disappointed, I turned my attention back to birdwatching. "The only essential equipment for seeing birds is a pair of eyes," my guidebook said. I ate blue popsicles and chewed Asper-Gum. Our house filled with the sounds of repair: drills, saws, large things being torn apart. I watched.

"The phoebe," my mother, Phoebe, announced drunkenly, "is the only bird who says its name."

We were hosting the welcome party for the Bishops. All the parties in those days were the same. Vats of vegetarian food—hummus and lasagna and tabouleh. Down on Atlantic Avenue Middle-Eastern stores lined the street and supplied our neighborhood with all of its hors d'ouevres. The adults drank jugs of chianti, talked too loudly, burned thick candles everywhere, played old Bob Dylan albums, sang Simon and Garfunkel songs until their voices cracked. The Bishops didn't know what to make of any of it.

"It's true," my mother insisted. "The phoebe is unique that way."

Mr. Bishop, who had been aloof and maybe even bored the entire night, said suddenly and loudly, "Bobwhite! Bobwhite!" He said it like a challenge, in a booming voice.

My mother laughed. "Excuse me?" she said. Whenever she drank too much wine she grew an accent like the Queen of England.

"The bobwhite, darling," Mr. Bishop said, leaning his tall frame until his face was very close to hers. "The bobwhite says its name."

Of course everyone was watching. Already no one much liked the Bishops. He drank scotch all night and refused the lasagna; he was a playwright who had come here from California. His wife had murder in her past, which explained the terrified look she wore. Her entire family—parents and two brothers—had been famously killed while they slept in their suburban Ohio home; Mrs. Bishop was away at college. She was an artist of some kind, a dancer or a poet, mysterious and sad. Mr. Bishop, Colin, was tall and hawk-nosed, but his wife was small and slender with thick wavy red hair. Her name was Babe.

"They're quails, you know," Mr. Bishop told my mother as if he were sharing a great confidence.

From where I sat, bored and sleepy, my throat still aching, on our brown corduroy bean bag, I could see that Mr. Bishop had one ear pierced and wore a diamond stud in it.

"Honestly," my mother said, all *la-di-dah*, "I don't know one fucking thing about birds."

Mr. Bishop thought this was the funniest thing ever. He laughed long and hard, still way too close to my mother, who smiled up at him.

"Do you know anything about stained-glass windows?" Mrs. Randall was asking Mrs. Bishop. That's how Mrs. Randall was, relentless. At her house she never left you alone, always plying you with her homemade granola or iced tea with soggy mint leaves floating in it. "Because I believe this one could be a Tiffany. An original. The amethyst and topaz colors are as rich as any I've seen in the books. Maybe you could come and look at it? Maybe tomorrow?"

"I don't know," Mrs. Bishop said, trying to catch her husband's attention. But he only had eyes for my mother. He had kneeled down at her side and the two of them, heads bent toward each other, were talking quietly.

"I won't hold you to it," Mrs. Randall said. "Just a look-see."

My father stood in the corner with two other men who also worked in Manhattan. He went off to teach Earth Science at City College; Mr. Randall was in advertising, like Darren on *Bewitched*, and he had the same buggy eyes and nervous sweaty look about him as Darren; Mr. Markowitz worked in book publishing and liked to toss around the names of writers everyone was supposed to have read but who my mother always dismissed as shlocky. Whenever they got together, which was almost every weekend, after they discussed grouting and wholesale tile warehouses, they talked about how wonderful Brooklyn was, as if they were trying to convince each other that was true.

The walls in this room were streaked at least a dozen different colors, from beige to buttercream. We were living with them to see which one suited us before we painted the room. My father stood in front of the lightest streaks, the beige and ivory and antique white. But my mother and Mr. Bishop were nearest the bright yellows, the ones we had already discarded as silly. Yet that night, at least from where I sat, those yellows seemed to illuminate my mother's face, to cast a light, in fact, around the two of them.

"Birds are grouped into orders, families, and genera according to similarities of bills, feet, and internal anatomy," my guidebook said. "If you know these groups, the relationship and classification of birds will be clearer." So I set about memorizing the groups. Herons and bitterns; plovers and snipes; hummingbirds and woodpeckers; hawks, eagles, and vultures. I liked to memorize things. I knew every birthstone for every month, for example, and pestered people to quiz me.

My mother didn't usually indulge me. But my father would happily ask, "August?" and beam when I answered, "Peridot." I knew the birthdays of rock stars, the dates famous people died in plane crashes (Jim Croce, Carole Lombard, Glenn Miller), the dates and personality characteristics of every astrological sign.

"Your scientific name," I told my mother, "is *Sayornis phoebe*."

"Great," she said. "Terrific." She was working on plans for a porch. My father did not pay attention to her desire for a porch in the back of the house. We need plumbing, he would say. We need electricity on the third floor. We need to fix the goddamn holes in the walls and all you can think about is a porch?

Finally, spring had arrived with thick hot air and too-bright sunshine. In our curtainless kitchen, all that light made everything seem even worse than it was. The old appliances sat away from the walls, unplugged and uncleaned. Half of the linoleum was curled back, exposing not a lovely hardwood floor but speckled concrete. We were in the process of tearing down two walls which left every surface covered with a thin veneer of plaster. For the next two weeks, we were eating only cold food or takeout.

For lunch, my mother had opened a bag of Fritos and a can of devilled ham. The Fritos hurt my throat. My new tonsillectomy date was May 4th, in just ten days. My mother had ordered me to stay healthy.

"Do you know the scientific name for a blue jay?" I asked my mother.

She kept drawing. "Honey," she said, "I don't care." Even though she had quit smoking years earlier, she had very recently started up again. But she lit cigarettes and then seemed to forget she was a smoker, leaving them to burn on the edge of the kitchen sink or in one of the shells we'd brought home from our vacation in Cape May last summer. A curl of smoke from her forgotten Salem drifted in front of her.

"*Cyanocitta cristata*," I told her.

She looked up, as if she just realized I was there. "I forgot," she said. "We're having dinner at the Bishops' tonight. Just us. Colin doesn't like big neighborhood things." She noticed her cigarette then and took a halfhearted puff. "Oh," she said. "Maybe you can make friends with the daughters. I think they're lonely."

"They wear flip-flops to school," I said.

She smiled. "Do they? Is that allowed?"

"Everything's allowed," I mumbled. My school was a progressive co-operative school, which meant parents were always lurking around and we spent more time expressing ourselves than learning real school things. We baked bread and kept a sad little vegetable garden, we cooked spaghetti on Fridays and dressed in traditional Vietnam folk costumes to celebrate Tet. Flip-flops were not going to cause much of a stir there. I changed tactics. "Fiona smokes pot," I said.

My mother laughed. "What is she? Thirteen? Please, Alice. Don't be so dramatic."

"*Colinus virginianus,*" I said.

"What?"

"That's the bobwhite," I said, waiting for a reaction. But she was already gone, back to her dreams of a porch.

In some ways, Brooklyn was exciting. For one thing, we had a yard. For another, suspicious looking people roamed the periphery of the streets, adding a sense of danger that had been missing on West 12th Street. As for birds, however, Brooklyn was disappointing. Still, I sat, binoculars in hand, watching and waiting for a discovery. Through the pink and white blossoms of the dogwood trees, planted by the Neighborhood Association, I could just make out the Bishops' second floor. Mrs. Bishop was painting there. All day she painted. I could see the tumble of her blond hair, the motion of her arms as she worked.

Mr. Bishop slept. He was in Manhattan at rehearsals of his play until late into the night. Sometimes I heard a taxi door slam and I would open my eyes to see the silver light of dawn covering our street. His play was done in the nude by three naked actors sitting on the edge of a Dumpster. It was about politics and ideas. No one understood any of it, although my mother had announced that Colin Bishop was a genius.

I watched a robin tend her three perfect blue ovals of eggs. Beyond the nest, I saw Mr. Bishop, shirtless, in the kitchen, finally awake. It was four o'clock in the afternoon. My father left the house at six-thirty in the morning, smelling of Irish Spring soap and shoe polish. He returned twelve hours later. I could set a watch by my father's comings and goings. He was predictable, someone a person could count on. I knew that at seven o'clock he watched the news with Roger Grimsby and drank a Heineken straight out of its green bottle. I knew that he read *Time* magazine in the bathroom, keeping them neatly stacked on the back of the toilet where they would wrinkle from dampness. I knew that on Saturday mornings he jogged around Prospect Park even if it was raining or freezing or humid and hot. He came home with bagels and orange juice and the newspaper; I could rely on that.

But what about a person like Mr. Bishop? A person who stayed out all night with naked people sitting on Dumpsters in warehouses south of Houston Street? A person who slept all day and walked around the house naked maybe? He was a person with no roots. He had migrated here from California via Chicago and Minneapolis and who knew where else. What could Fiona and Imogen depend on him for? What could Mrs. Bishop rely on? The ground beneath their brownstone seemed shaky to me. No matter how much Mrs. Bishop painted, I wondered what she could possibly hope for in the end.

My father brought a dark green box with a gold bow on top to dinner at the Bishops' that night.

"How does he afford this stuff?" he mumbled as we crossed the street. "It's pretentious, if you want to ask me."

My mother rolled her eyes and smoothed her skirt. My father hated that skirt, a long thing with rows of different material. He thought she looked silly in it. She hated his bow ties. My students get a kick out of them, he told her. If I closed my eyes I could recite the order of the fabric: red and yellow flowers, black corduroy, green and gold paisley, denim, blue and white boat-striped, and then a final black velvet ruffle. She always wore it with a white pocket T-shirt tucked into the waist, and a fat belt of large silver discs connected by rope.

"Why did you wear that thing?" my father said. He didn't expect an answer. He rang the doorbell and stared hard at the front door, which had been stripped of paint and stood bare before us.

Fiona opened the door. She was stoned, even I knew that, and I'd only had two of the required drug-education classes at school. Her eyes were heavy lidded and she wore a stupid grin. Also, she smelled of pot. In our school, the playground was a drug paradise, with pills and hashish and pot getting traded the way the younger kids traded baseball cards.

"Hey," she said, and smiled at us. Fiona's teeth were beautiful and white and straight. The boys all loved her, with those teeth and that pale blond hair.

We followed her through a labyrinth of empty rooms to the kitchen. Unlike everyone else we knew, the Bishops had done their kitchen first, and after the chipped paint and scuffed floors we'd passed on our way, the kitchen positively dazzled us. A double slate sink. Marble floor. A library table set with dishes the color of dangerous things like maraschino cherries and orange nuclear waste. At the six-burner Glenwood stove stood not Mrs. Bishop, but Mr. Bishop, stirring and tasting. I had never seen my father cook anything. My mother even grilled the hamburgers and hot dogs in the summer. But Mr. Bishop looked relaxed and in charge. He was drinking wine from a water glass and when he saw us, after he shook hands with my father and hugged my mother, he poured them each a glass, too.

My mother elbowed me toward Fiona, who was staring at us blankly.

"Why don't you show Alice around?" she said to Fiona. "I know she'd like to see your room."

I groaned.

"Okay," Fiona said in her placid voice.

The kitchen was warm and smelled of garlic and exotic spices. I didn't want to leave it. But I once again followed Fiona, this time upstairs to her room. Instead of a door, a curtain of beads hung in the doorway. She parted it for me and then flopped onto her bed, which was really just a mattress on the floor, covered with Indian bedspreads.

"You like Jethro Tull?" she said, putting the arm down on an album before I could answer. "*Aqualung,*" she said. She sighed. "We won't be here long. We just sort of, you know." She moved her hands like a hula dancer and smiled to herself. "Pass through. Usually my father does something terrible and there's some kind of scene." She squinted up at me. "I bet your father never makes a scene."

"I don't know," I said, shrugging.

"I bet your mother does though. Right?" Before I could answer she said, "Isn't this flute like, so, I don't know."

Then she closed her eyes and moved her head in time with the music.

I listened but I didn't like the music. There was nothing to look at in the room. No posters on the wall. No place for me to sit, unless I climbed on the mattress beside Fiona, which seemed uncool. I stood awkwardly by the curtain of beads, until I realized that Fiona had actually drifted off to sleep. Her breathing was slow and even. "Fiona?" I said softly. But she didn't wake up.

As quietly as I could, I moved between the beads and out into the hallway. Leaning against the wall were framed posters from museum shows in London and Los Angeles and Chicago. All the doors were shut except for one room where the door was off its hinges and propped at an odd angle in the frame. I stepped inside.

Mrs. Bishop was in there painting. This was the room I could see from my bedroom and now I saw what was taking her so long. She was painting a mural that spread across all four walls, a mural of a garden filled with bright flowers—asters and zinnias and dahlias and marigolds—all of them thick with paint and color, oranges and yellows and purples and reds.

She didn't stop painting when I walked in. She said, "Oh? Is it dinner already?"

"I don't know," I said. "I was just looking around."

"Find anything interesting?" she said. She was working on a section of tulips.

"This is pretty interesting," I said.

"I always paint a garden in a new house. Always," she said.

I nodded. I was thinking about birds, how their bills developed depending on the food they ate. The shrike, the cardinal, the wood thrush, the crossbill, the yellow throat were all in the same family, yet their bills all looked different.

Mrs. Bishop looked up then and smiled. Her teeth were horsey and big, but they only added to her unique look. "I guess we should see what's cooking, hmmm?"

My mother would have showered and primped before joining her guests. But Mrs. Bishop didn't bother. She stayed in her paint splattered clothes, her hair in a messy ponytail, without even bothering to put on shoes. When we walked into the kitchen, my mother smiled her Queen Elizabeth smile.

"Babe," she said. "I was wondering where you were."

My father sat at the table eating olives and looking miserable.

"Upstairs," Mrs. Bishop said.

"She'll have to show you her masterpiece sometime," Mr. Bishop said.

I wanted to say that it was beautiful, but something stopped me. Perhaps it was the way Mr. Bishop had said the word masterpiece. Or the way my mother smiled when he did. Or maybe it was just the air in the kitchen that night, which seemed oddly charged, the way the air feels just before a cold front moves in.

One day to my tonsillectomy and I spiked a fever during School Meeting. In School Meeting, all the sixth, seventh, and eighth graders sat on colorful cushions in the Activity Room and aired our feelings. Susan Markowitz wanted to talk about male chauvinism, how the boys dominated certain areas of the school. Trini Randall wanted to discuss changing the morning snack from peanut butter and crackers to fruit and nuts. Fiona Bishop used her red cushion as a pillow, stretched out with her head on it, and went to sleep.

I raised my hand.

"Alice?" said Bob, my literature teacher.

"My throat hurts. It feels like I have razor blades in it."

The health teacher, Patty, came over to me and touched my forehead with her large cool hand. "You have a temperature," she said.

"Do you want me to call your mom?

"I'll just go home by myself," I said.

"Do you want Trini to walk with you?"

I shook my head. As I gathered my things, I heard Felix Crawley saying that the school should write a letter to the president about the MIAs. Once, at a Saturday night dinner at the Crawley's, I had let Felix French kiss me. Now his voice made me nauseated. His tongue had felt cold and slimy and ever since I had hated him. With my head hurting and my throat sore, I practically ran out of there and the six blocks home, past the bodega with its weird chicken smells and the Irish bar with its stale beer smell and the head shop with its strong incense and B.O. smell. Finally I was home and all I could think of was a blue popsicle and TV game shows.

But when I pushed into the kitchen I found my mother and Mr. Bishop eating Chinese food and drinking my father's Heineken.

"Oh, no," my mother said when she saw me. "Not your throat."

She had a smear of brown sauce on her cheek, as if she'd been sticking her whole face in the white cartons of food. When she reached her hand out to touch my forehead, I pulled away.

"What's the matter with her throat?" Mr. Bishop said. He was eating the food with long green chopsticks, and they hung in the air like daggers.

"It's her tonsils," my mother said, exasperated. "She was supposed to finally have them out tomorrow but they can't operate if they're infected." She stood up and sighed. "I'll have to call Doctor Williams again and cancel. Get you some antibiotics."

Mr. Bishop took hold of her wrist. "Phoebe, don't you know that antibiotics are poisoning us? Really they are. Soon they won't even work anymore and new mutant bacteria will kill us all."

She sat back down. He didn't let go of her wrist. "Do you know about the Bach Flower Remedies?"

My mother shook her head. The way she looked at Mr. Bishop made me uncomfortable, like I shouldn't be there. I rummaged in the freezer for a stray popsicle.

"Doctor Edward Bach discovered them in England in the thirties.

Thirty-eight different flowers for various characteristics and emotions. Let me bring some by for Alice tomorrow."

"We're out of popsicles," I said.

"Yes, bring them," my mother said. "You're absolutely right. The antibiotics aren't doing a thing."

Every day for a week Mr. Bishop arrived at one o'clock with a combination of cherry plum, clematis, impatiens, rock rose, and star of Bethlehem in a vial with an eye dropper. He placed four drops on my tongue while I glared at him through my feverish eyes. "I need medicine," I croaked, my throat worse every day.

After he left I propped my pillows up so I could watch the mother robin feeding her newly hatched babies. They were ugly, those babies, like Martians. But she tended them carefully, bringing them worms and bugs to eat, flapping her wings whenever she arrived.

My mother cooked all morning, preparing for Mr. Bishop's visit. I would hear her downstairs in the kitchen, the clanging of lids on pots, the whir of her Cuisinart, the one my father had surprised her with last Christmas. Then strange smells drifted up to my bedroom. Mr. Bishop liked Italian food. Not the kind we ate at Rossini's in the Village, but another kind with no red sauce or melted cheese. She made him a special rice that required her to stand at the stove and stir it constantly, adding small amounts of warm broth at certain intervals. When I called down in my hoarse voice for ginger ale, she answered, "I can't leave the risotto, Alice!" She roasted pork with sprigs of rosemary that looked like part of the robin's nest outside my window. She sautéed sweetbreads, which were not bread at all but rather the internal organs of some animal. The smells made me gag.

So did the drops of rescue remedy that Mr. Bishop administered. My tongue felt swollen and burned by them. He looked solemn afterwards.

"Alice," he said each time, "you are on the road to recovery. Wait and see."

Then he'd screw the lid back on the vial and go downstairs where he and my mother ate for hours. I listened to the lilt and murmur of their voices, hating both of them. From my window I watched him leave for the theatre, and watched my father walk up our street a few hours later, precisely at six thirty. My mother served him leftovers, reheated, and sat at the table smoking cigarettes, watching as he ate.

Unbelievably, I awoke one morning a week after Mr. Bishop began treating me with the Bach Flower Remedy, cured. I swallowed easily. I spoke clearly. It was a glorious warm day and the sun was bright and yellow in the sky. My mother had already begun making lunch for Mr. Bishop. She sat at the kitchen table, hand grating from a big wheel of stinky cheese. I slipped out unnoticed, my binoculars around my neck and my birding notebook in my hand.

Last week I had done an oral report in school on ornithology. The topic was "My Hobby." Trini Randall gave a talk on ikibani, the art of Japanese flower arranging. She had taken a class on it at the Botanical Garden. Felix gave his on collecting bottlecaps. He had shown a cigar box painted in splatter paint and filled with bottlecaps he found on the streets of our neighborhood. But my report was the best because ornithology really was my hobby and I really had started to love it. Unlike meteorology, ornithology taught useful skills. The skills of observation. The powers of deduction.

"Bird watching is exciting," I'd said, "because birds are easy to see, easy to identify, great in numbers and variety, beautiful to observe, and attractive to hear."

On this May morning, as I walked into Prospect Park, the trill and chirp of various birds filled my ears. I could make out the birds singing each song, the black-throated green warbler, the chickadee, and the wood thrush with its clear, flute-like sound. I stood beneath the blooming trees and lifted my face upward where the birds perched high above me.

Something caught my eye. At first, I thought it was a crow. But then I saw its yellow bill. My mind raced through all the birds I had memorized, alphabetically, the red-eyed vireo and scarlet tanager, the northern cardinal and rose-breasted grosbeak. But it was none of these. I was

almost certain that I was looking at a yellow-billed magpie, a bird
that did not migrate east. I stood staring up at that bird until my neck
ached and my fingers gripping the binoculars grew numb. A yellow-
billed magpie, I knew, had no reason to be in Brooklyn, New York.

I recorded my observations in my notebook, then slowly made my
way home, imagining how I would call my local bird-watching club
and report my discovery. Maybe I would even get on the news with
Roger Grimsby. I could see myself in Prospect Park, under the trees,
getting interviewed live. I could warn the population of Park Slope
about the yellow-billed magpie. With its impressive sweeping tail, it
was easy to admire. But like its cousin the crow, it could easily become a pest. Roger Grimsby and all of New York City would be
impressed by my knowledge.

At my front door I paused. A small bundle of dried grass lay at the
foot of the steps. With my toe I lifted the grass and saw that this was
the nest I had watched all these weeks. The smallest slivers of blue
eggshell still clung in places. But the birds were gone. They had flown
away. Carefully, I picked up the nest, unsure of what else to do, and
carried it inside with me.

At the grand staircase that led upstairs, I stood still, listening to the
voices of my mother and Mr. Bishop from somewhere in the house.

"Pine," he was saying, "to rid you of guilt. Honeysuckle to keep
you from living in the past."

I heard this and understood he had brought her a remedy, too.

Since we'd moved in here, the house had smelled of paint and plaster, of cottonseed oil and sawdust. But as I stood holding that nest, the
air smelled unfamiliar, like the strange Italian food my mother had
been cooking, and other unfamiliar smells, things I could not identify.

The excitement of my discovery began to fade. Gently, I placed the
nest on the bottom step. These stairs had been covered in dark orange
indoor-outdoor carpeting when we'd moved in. My parents had spent
hours on their hands and knees, removing it from the stairs and marveling at the fine wood beneath it. I could still see the circular motion of my mother's hands as she nourished the wood, sanding it,
then oiling it, until it gleamed like it did now.

I stepped outside, empty handed, and looked up and down the street, at the brownstones that needed repair, every one of them broken in some way. Nothing looked the same to me. I sat on the stoop and waited. Whether for my mother to come out, or my father to turn the corner, I could not say.

Barcelona, 1968: with Mom and Dad on my first trip to Spain, where my mother was born and raised. This shot was taken on an apartment balcony belonging to my mother's aunt and uncle. The street below was once used to herd cows to a nearby slaughterhouse. Many years after this visit, I would stand on the same balcony and listen to Bruce Springsteen records blaring from a café across the street.

Andrew Roe lives in Northern California. His articles and book reviews have appeared in the *San Francisco Chronicle*, the *New York Times*, *Salon.com*, and other publications. He is currently working on a novel.

ROUGH

Andrew Roe

Anna told Aaron that she liked it kind of rough. They were walking back to his apartment, mildly drunk, shuddering against the streaming fog and cold. He wasn't sure what that meant exactly, "kind of rough"—but he didn't want to disrupt the flow of the potentially epic evening (so far so good) with stupid questions that would reveal his staggeringly sedate suburban roots and quasi-conservative leanings (shit, he'd voted for Bush, both of them, actually), which he still felt vaguely embarrassed about even after having lived in the famously liberal city—The City—for close to seven years now. That's what they called it here, The City, capital "T," capital "C," as in "I've been living in The City for close to seven years now," as if there was only one city and where else would you live?

As it turned out, though, whether or not Aaron was sexually qualified in the rough department didn't really matter. After a poorly executed elevator kiss (his initial overture drew ear and hair instead of lips), and after opening a bottle of blueberry Schnapps (the only alcoholic beverage he could forage in the kitchen; it was either that or NyQuil), and engaging in some subsequent sofa groping and minimalist dialogue right before (Should I?... There... How's that?... Maybe if... Okay, good...), he came in like five seconds and then it was over.

"So much for rough," he said, going for levity, because at that point what else could he do? And then because she didn't say anything back right away he added, "It's been a while."

"Me too," she said.

Aaron's brother gave the toast at the wedding. He was in A.A. so he didn't raise a glass of champagne. He raised a glass of water instead. The speech incorporated all the standard themes and conventions of the rather limited wedding-speech genre—the use of humor and embarrassment mixed, ultimately, when it came time for the 150 or so guests to uniformly hoist their glasses upward and wish the happy couple the best, with sincerity; covering Aaron's non-traumatic childhood, his bumbling yet endearing adolescence and teenage years, his partying college days (and here Aaron's brother inserted a cautionary note about the perils of excessive drinking, offering himself as an example), and his eventual relocation to The City—except Aaron's brother, being a lifelong Midwesterner, made the faux pas of saying the actual name—and then bringing in Anna, what a great girl she was, and how she made such a great addition to the whole curmudgeonly Cahill clan, and of course ending with the final thought of how now there was one family instead of two, etc.

Everyone agreed that the wedding was a major success (although, granted, the goateed deejay ignored Aaron and Anna's emphatic request *not* to play "Y.M.C.A."). Guests mingled easily, naturally; trays carrying wine and hors d'oeuvres kept appearing just when more food and drink was needed, as if on cue; time slowed to a tranquil, celebratory hum; and the outside world temporarily receded away like a spent wave returning to the ocean. There was one point during the reception when Anna looked across the room to see Aaron talking to a pregnant cousin of his, and then he turned, and their eyes met at just the right time, and it was one of those totally clichéd yet very real cinematic moments (complete with orchestral soundtrack swelling in the background, or so it seemed to their mutual internal stereo system), where everything falls into place and you know you're doing the right thing and that people are meant for each other and, no, we're not all essentially alone, and, yes, a life can in fact be shared, truly, wholly, deeply.

Why do we say what we say, do what we do? Can reason and motive and certainty ever be completely confirmed? How does love begin? How does it end? Does it end at all? What, if anything, lasts? This was the babbling brook of thoughts and questions that flowed through her on the cab ride home, still dark, the city still asleep, but the night just about ready to expire, to become something else, the sky slowly lightening.

She didn't know why she said she liked it rough, which wasn't true, which was just a dumbshit line that came to her, an utterance penned by someone else and that slipped out by mistake. It was something to say when you're tipsy from too many cosmopolitans and your body is alive with the electric blood-buzz of discovering a new person (a very *promising* new person), and you're walking past elaborate mansions that no doubt house elaborate lives, and in the distance there's the bay's steadfast foghorn lament and the occasional cable car clank, and you're periodically looking at him and thinking a million different things and then only one thing.

Afterwards he was sweet, offering her tea and control of the remote. But she didn't stay, and she could tell the decision made it worse for him. Immediately she regretted it—"I think I should go," which became the harshest sentence she'd ever spoken—but it was too late. And plus she really did want to go. She suddenly had the postcoital—if you could even call it that—desire to be alone.

It wasn't like this hadn't ever happened before. She had a boyfriend in college who'd been that way, chronically, who'd even read up on the subject to try to increase his stamina. One tactic he tried was to masturbate while watching himself in the mirror and then stop right before he came. Which didn't work. Neither did thinking of sports or Bea Arthur or the ghastly shrunken old woman who replenished the salad bar in the school cafeteria.

She remembered, too, a film appreciation class she'd taken in college, and one of the films they appreciated was *The French Lieutenant's Woman*. According to her professor, the sex scene in the movie represented the most realistic sex scene ever put on film. Why? Because after Jeremy Irons has endured all this unbearable pent-up passion and stinging desire for Meryl Streep, he finally gets his chance to fuck her and he comes in like five seconds and then it's over. He didn't say anything about it having been a while, although that was probably the case, it being Victorian England and all.

Seconds, minutes, an hour—what did it matter, really? It was all transitory, over before you knew it, she thought. There were other things to consider.

He never saw himself as the type to videotape the birth of his children, but he'd done it for all three. In fact, he became something of a delivery-room auteur, jockeying around nurses and orderlies and anesthesiologists to get the best angles, making use of natural lighting, trying to create a Scorcese-inspired gritty realism and edginess. When reviewing the tapes he could see a definite progression in his work, from the first birth to the final one—and it was the final one. There'd be no more kids, they'd decided, no more home movies of blood and birth and beauty. Three was enough.

By then they no longer lived in The City, but in a house in a city (a suburb, that is) where it was okay to say the name. They had neighbors who always waved, gym memberships that did not go unused, financial portfolios with mutual funds that were considered "moderate aggressive." He felt lucky. He was lucky. Sometimes he'd sit in the backyard and soak in the multicolored sunset and pleasantly marvel at the simplicity, the fundamental ordinariness of his life. He'd playfully pat his ebbing stomach and not worry too much about its slow yet determined expansion. He'd see Anna inside the house, knowing that she'd eventually come outside to join him. He loved the waiting, the anticipation of that, knowing that soon he would reach out to touch her and she would touch back. His wife. They'd come a long way since that bar in the Marina. Every year they went there and had a drink to celebrate the anniversary of their first date.

It did not look good. It did not look good at all. He stayed up until it got light, unsuccessfully trying to console himself in the numbing whirl of late-night/early-morning cable until his eyes stung too much and he could no longer watch.

In the afternoon he made coffee. While it was brewing, he walked to the café around the corner to get one of those big-ass poppyseed muffins he liked so much. It was all part of his Sunday ritual. He went back to his apartment and read the paper. Twice. Even the travel section. He listened to early R.E.M. and thought about a screenplay that he knew he'd never write. Which was also part of the ritual.

He would see Anna the next day. They worked together, after all. Well, not really together, but at the same company, along with about a thousand other people. They had little work-related interaction, a fact that now made him grateful. They'd struck up a conversation at the office Christmas party a week before. Hence the date. Hence the fuck that was over before it began.

People started dying. Parents, uncles, aunts, coworkers. Even neighbors. Mr. Tillman, for instance, who only a year ago was running in 10Ks and doing tai chi at the nearby park (he once showed Aaron a few of the moves, the names of which still stuck with him: Cloud Hands, Grasp Swallow's Tail, Parting Horse's Mane, Sleeves Dancing Like Plum Blossoms). Cancer, of course. You could see how utterly devastated Mrs. Tillman was. Then she died too. And plus there were the more random, middle-aged, you-can't-fucking-believe-it deaths: Terry Finkel, car accident; Jenny Blackstock, also cancer, breast; Dave Gingrass, some kind of ski-lift accident in Austria. And even kids, teenagers, which was the worst. Through it all, they held each other closer, tighter. They didn't sleep as well as they used to (had they ever slept well?), especially when they knew their two daughters and one son, all full-fledged teenagers now, one about to leave for college and seriously considering becoming a vegetarian, were out, away, doing things they didn't want to know about—but of course they did want to know, and that was part of it too, the wanting to know and the not wanting to know. It could happen no matter how good you were, no matter how you lived your life. No big revelation here, they admitted, but still, it made you think. How terminally fragile life was, is. It was true: Being a parent changes everything. Your children—they become everything. You make them but then they remake you. And then they leave.

That afternoon she canceled her plans to catch a movie with a friend. Instead she stayed in, writing letters, doing laundry, enjoying the lonely hum of Sunday. The weather was shitty anyway, and what else was new, the fog pouring in as if propelled from a hidden machine. She saw it from her apartment window, pulsing with what seemed to be a secret purpose, the wind bowing back the trees and swirling garbage and dust. (Anna lived three blocks from the ocean, in the Sunset District, where the sun could disappear for weeks on end. Fogville, she called it, which, sure, eventually got to you psychologically, but she'd been desperate to find a place and had unfortunately signed a yearlong lease.) Repeatedly, she tortured herself by playing the night back in her mind. Fuck. She shouldn't have left. Why did she leave? She should have stayed. Everything would have been better if she had stayed. Now there would be this awkwardness, because of that, and because of Aaron's, well, brevity. Fuck. Would it have killed her to stay, to lie in his arms and wake up together and then maybe even go out to breakfast and talk about how they've both always wanted a house with a porch and isn't Cormac McCarthy amazing?

The last few men she'd dated were fond of wearing black (and nothing but black) and hanging postcards of obscure Latin American poets on their bedroom walls. So that's why Aaron seemed like such a breath of fresh air. She was just beginning to think she only attracted a certain kind of guy: angst-ridden, distant, unable to accept their anonymity in the world. They usually played in bands or were trying to start bands. Aaron did not play an instrument and he did not quote Rilke. He was from Ohio.

One of her coworkers, Cheryl from Product Development, had pointed him out to her. "Hottie alert," Cheryl had said as Aaron approached, and then passed them on his way to the kitchen.

Anna usually didn't pay much attention to what Cheryl said. She was one of those women who Anna had decided to tune out—the kind who were always criticizing other women as too fat, too thin, too slutty, too librarian. But she was right about Aaron. He made her tingle in all the right places.

When she saw him at the Christmas party she hesitated about going over to talk to him. She felt that high-school dorkiness that had never left her completely, especially when it came to situations such as this. *Just do it. After all, this could be your husband*, was the weird random thought that whispered its way into her head, one of those out-of-the-blue aberrations that you think of every now and then because at some point in your life it's going to be true, it will be your husband. *Think of something dazzling to say so you'll have a good story to tell your kids.* Then she laughed to herself. But she didn't have to do anything: he was the one who came over to her. She told herself to remember what song was playing as he made his way toward her, but she got so involved in the conversation, and so taken by his smile (genuine, sexy, a little shy), that she forgot.

There are mysteries, though. He had to admit that. No matter how close you think you are, no matter how truly double-helixed your lives seem to be, you can't know everything. Secrets exist, uncertainties linger. Inevitably there are those things that get lost along the years, that happen and somehow are never picked up again. Like what she said the night of their first date: How she liked it rough. What was that all about? They'd never discussed it, not once in all these years and decades together (there were grandchildren now, the mortgage paid off, a second home in Lake Tahoe, etc.). It had passed. It had simply passed. Although somehow it had haunted them, too. At least it had haunted him. He wondered periodically over the years, whenever there was an especially long silence or when they felt out of sync and foreign to each other, if she was thinking of that, how they'd never talked about it, how she'd liked it rough and she'd never had it rough all these years.

She hadn't wanted to die in a hospital. So they brought her home. They gathered around the bed—their bed—and took turns gently pressing ice cubes to her mouth, to moisten the perpetual dryness.

"Dad," his children said. "Don't stay up too late. Get some rest, 'kay?" Then he was alone with her. Somehow, he knew. He sat and smelled her smell and remembered as much as he could and watched the last breath of air escape from her lips. Then he kissed them one last time.

All right: he told himself not to dwell on it on the bus ride to work, but of course he did. His only distraction was the woman standing next to him. She was stunning. Occasionally the sway of the crowded bus caused their shoulders to haphazardly rub, and every time it happened a pinching little ache bloomed in Aaron's chest. Was she thinking the same thing he was, which was this: what if they started talking? What if he made some comment about the book she was reading (a thick fucking doorstop of a novel, something called *Underworld*), and then that spurred a conversation and it went so well that they exchanged e-mail addresses (safer, better than phone numbers), and that led to a date and another date, and isn't it funny how love can strike where you least expect it, like for example a rush-hour bus that reeked of old bread and had no empty seats, and because of this, the lack of seating, they happened to be standing next to each other on a certain day at a certain time… But he didn't say anything, and neither did she. And his would-be wife/lover/soul mate/mother of his children got off at the exit before his and he watched her disappear into the downtown crowd, lost forever, his life completely altering in a space of five seconds, and then returning back to the way it was. He often had these inwardly dramatic commutes. And Mondays were particularly fertile for such imaginings and longings.

First thing at work, he got settled in for the week, checking his e-mail, returning phone calls, planning out his calendar. He wasn't ready to do any real work yet. He was easing into the day, pacing himself. And all the while Anna hovered in the back of his mind like a bad movie he'd seen a few days ago but couldn't stop thinking of. How would he approach her? What would he say? How would she react? Where was the best place to talk to her?

She worked on the other side of the floor. Her cube had an actual view. You could make out part of the Bay Bridge, the stream of cars and invisible commuters constant, never ending. People driving no matter what. He still wasn't clear on her job and what she did exactly. Some kind of market research, he thought uncertainly. When time for lunch rolled around he hadn't walked over. He decided to let it go a little while longer, to see how the afternoon developed.

But not long after making that decision (or rather nondecision), he was proofreading a report on the ability of young children to recognize company mascots and logos and then there she was, standing at his cube.

"Hey," she said.

"Hey," he said.

"Have you had lunch yet?"

"No, I was just starting to think about it, though."

There was something in her eyes, her entire face, even—a look. A definite look that said yes, maybe something could happen here, it wasn't too late. He told himself not to stare, to continue to use language and stand up and grab his jacket and ask where she wanted to go, what she felt like eating. But the look paralyzed him. He just sat there, happy. At least now there seemed to be, if nothing else, the possibility of the possible. It gave him hope.

I like the calm expression in this picture.

Kelly Malone earned an MFA from Warren Wilson College. She lives with her husband, son, and dog in Seattle, Washington, where she writes and works as an editor.

AVÓ

Kelly Malone

Kelly Malone

M y mother dumping me off for the first time. Racing through the valley dust in her new '66 Mustang, folding a piece of black gum into her mouth before inhaling from her L&M, saying as she exhales, "You'll be fine. We'll all be dandy. Now get your hand away from your face. We're here."

My grandfather stands on the farmhouse porch in work pants and a battered suit coat. My avó pats the thinning bun she wears at the nape of her neck, smooths it until my grandfather tucks his arm through hers, when she leaves her hair to work her rosary—third one from the left of the group hanging from her belt.

My mother looks straight at my grandfather. "You touch my daughter, old man, and I'll break your arm."

"Did someone say something?" he asks his wife. "Are the horseflies buzzing again?"

My mother clutches me in a bone-crunching hug, soaking me in the spice-heavy perfume that Gus gave her because it reminds him of his ex-wife. She lets go, pushing me out of range, backs toward the car, her eyes on me. Black holes, my mother's eyes. "Get your act together, honey," she says. "You have the summer."

I fold my arms across my chest, cupping my elbows in my hands.

"Don't start with that 'I'm dissolving' business," she says.

Then her focus softens, and I know she's looking through me to the oak-stubbed hills, home. Where she'll drink Manhattans on the patio with my stepfather. Then she's pulling out of the drive, waving the entire way down the old dirt road. I'm surrounded. By bamboo and eucalyptus, breathing hot valley air and alfalfa fumes. I'm begging, *Pleasepleaseplease*, but I don't remember what I was asking for.

My mother always told me I was like my ex-father (her term). She'd divorced him five years earlier. She did not need his ghost in her new marriage, she said. I told her I had only my father's good characteristics. She said those numbered zero. I told her we were different, he and I. He drinks too much, I told her. Way more than I do. My mother looked around the room, as if she'd find help, then said, "Good Jesus, Marva. You're only fourteen. Drinking?"

That had sealed the fate on my summer. "Your grandmother will straighten you out," my mother said. "She's a saint, your avó."

The words "unlike your grandfather" went unsaid. Though as far as I could tell, my grandfather wasn't too bad. He gave me silver dollars on my birthday and showed me the gaps left by teeth he'd lost.

As for Vó, if sainthood meant working like a mule, then she qualified, cooking for the one meal a day my grandfather ate. All morning I helped her make soups, and goat cheese, and, after a week, *linguiça*, the Portuguese pork sausage she pickled and smoked in the shed where she made the wine. As my avó pulled the pork shoulder from the pickling brine and transferred it to the cutting board, fennel and laurel and green peppercorns confettied the table.

"Am I at all like you, Vó?" I asked.

She scraped the meat with the blade of her knife. "You no want to be like me. Understand?"

But I did. Want to be like her. "João then," I picked up my knife, "do I have his traits?" Not sure if I wanted to know if I resembled my grandfather, I began chopping the red chiles that had been seeded and stemmed.

She smiled at me. "Your hair," she said, "you have the same bush of it." Then she put down her knife, and took mine from me. "Here, *minha*, like this." The knife moved up and down, down and forward. She slid the blade through chilies. "You push, and what you're cutting moves from one side to the other." She added the chilies to an earthenware bowl, then mixed pork, chilies, garlic, roasted cumin seeds, and homemade vinegar before frying a sample in a cast-iron skillet.

I stood behind her, watching the fat spit, the colors deepen. "Did you love him when you were young?"

"Yes." Her eyes narrowed as she flipped the sausage, bright red with browning chunks of fat. She tasted a small piece of the cooked sausage and added salt.

"*Minha*," she said, "you must no have the preoccupation when you cook. It haunts the food, you understand?" She was always talking like that. Vó saw connections—between feelings and objects, this world and others. She had premonitions. She believed in fate. *Fado.*

Mojo jabber, Sylvia called it.

João was Vó's fate. She'd apprenticed as a cook in the kitchen of the Italian embassy on the island of Madeira. She'd loved the job, but after one year, she'd married my grandfather and moved to California, just as their families had planned. This, the rest of her life, was the aftermath she must endure.

The other day, when Vó had offered the old man a second serving of soup before he'd finished his first, he'd raised his hand in the air as though to strike. Her eyes had gleamed in righteousness. I knew the logic. The more she suffered quietly, the greater the proof of her worthiness.

"Is Sylvia like him?" I asked.

"He tried to make her to be like him. He kept her always home from the school to make chores with him."

"Is that why she's such a psycho-case?"

My avó stuffed a casing. "She has the preoccupations."

"Can you inherit that?" I gathered my dishes to take to the sink. "Preoccupation?"

Vó knotted the end of the casing, biting off the excess string. "You are like you, Marva."

I set the dishes to the sink. The answer calmed me for a minute before it brought me back to the beginning of the circle.

I think my grandfather saw Sylvia in me, saw what he thought of as her laziness. Try as I did—setting the clock, commanding myself before sleeping to wake at dawn—I could not get up by 6 A.M., let alone 4 A.M. when he rose. One morning, I woke to my grandparent's arguing in the kitchen. I sat up slowly on the living-room sofa, squinting at the clock—6 A.M. I heard my grandfather say the word "lazy." He muttered about my still being in bed that morning, sitting under the fig tree or in the old Plymouth and reading or listening to the transistor for hours whenever I wasn't cleaning or helping Vó cook for him.

"She is soft," João said. "*Não?*"

I picked my cut-off jeans from the floor and searched the pockets for the Pall Mall I had stolen from my grandfather. My grandparents didn't believe the recent warnings about cigarettes. They'd grown up on dairy farms. By the time they were twelve years old, they were rolling their own. If I had asked my grandfather for a cigarette, he would have said, "Help yourself, *leõzinha.*" He called me little lion because of my frizzed red hair. I hated my hair, felt it looked weird with my black brows, but that's what I'd been given.

I stood on the unpainted wood floor. My grandfather allowed no paint on the walls of his home. "We are not wasteful, silly people," he said. If he had allowed it, though, Vó would have brightened the rooms with vivid blues, coral, and yellow.

"Isn't that a good idea?" I heard João ask.

Vó did not answer.

I lit my cigarette, inhaled, exhaled, and scratched my mosquito-bitten calves. My grandfather, quieter now, spoke in Portuguese so I didn't understand much except for his swearing. "Goddamn it," he said in English, and "soong of a beesh." I hadn't heard my grandmother say a word. I pictured her, sitting at the oak table, stern, silent, mouth set, pious under the pictures of the Sacred Heart, the Last Supper, and FDR—the pictures framed, all of them, in imitation gold plate.

I heard Vó grating the lids on the wood stove, heard the *linguiça* sputtering in the cast-iron pan. I smelled coffee and almond wood smoke and the thick-sliced sourdough cornbread she had baked in the ashes and was grilling over the coals. If only João would leave so I could sit down to breakfast without him watching me devour his food.

"It's a good idea I have, old woman," João said. "*Não*? She can take over feeding the dogs. Giving them just enough food to keep them alive, watching them grow meaner at her hand, this will help her see how you have to be in this world." Vó was quiet. He grew louder until Vó finally broke and said, "Don't try it, you sorry I-don't-know-what." Then she whispered, "She's got too much of you in her already."

I sat down on the cot. I wouldn't starve the dogs. I'd have to deaden myself to do it, and I didn't think I could stand to numb myself anymore. I inhaled my cigarette until it scorched my lungs.

The back door squeaked shut as João left for the morning. I waited until I heard my avó go into the bathroom to bathe and get dressed, then I went to brush my teeth at the kitchen sink. There was such a sense of peace about Vó. I calmed just looking at the care she took with her house. Sunlight filled the room, shone on the rose-patterned linoleum she had glued down thirty years before and waxed diligently ever since. There was a mason jar full of peonies in the center of the table, and next to it, the breakfast Vó had laid out for me.

I sat down and spread my toast with homemade fig jam and the fresh goat cheese Vó had made in muslin-lined coffee cans. Vó came into the kitchen, and, as she walked behind me, on her way to the stove, she passed a cool, gnarled hand across the top of my head as she headed toward the stove, leaving the scent of violet water and licorice toothpaste. "Your mother telephoned to me last night after you were in bed. She cannot make the visit here for the Fourth of July."

"I was awake." I stared into my cup of coffee, at the greenish oils floating around the top, the oil my avó had taught me meant a perfectly proportioned brew.

"Ah." As she cooked, her shoulders dropped, relaxing.

"Do you want the sausage?"

"Sure," I told her, stirring my coffee with the same slow revolutions she used to blend the soup, waiting until I loosened, until I felt something give.

For the first few weeks, Vó let me sleep, but after my grandfather started talking about having me feed the dogs, she started waking me up early each morning, standing above my bed, whispering, "Sshhh." Shaking me. Sshhh. She wore her housecoat. Her hair was not yet twisted for the day, but worn down in the braid she wore to sleep in, in her own bed, behind her locked door. Loose strands tangled around her earrings—tiny, filigreed, in her pulled-down lobes.

"Come," she said, the first time I helped her feed the dogs. "João's giving them their meal. We will soon give them another."

Vó and I watched João from the service porch. She pressed her face against the rusted wire mesh of the back screen. Every morning, after his chores, after he'd fed the dogs, João followed the path through the bamboo to settle on the bank of the Merced river where he fished all day, had done so since he'd leased his fields to soybean farmers.

He didn't speak to the dogs when he fed them, just paused outside the dog pen to toss the chuck scraps to the dirt just beyond the animals' reach. We waited there, peering through the screen, Vó's back straight as she strummed the screen with her gnawed fingernails. He must have felt our glaring; he stopped for a minute—hand extended, mid-throw—then continued before turning toward the barn, never looking back at us or the two watchdogs, who rushed the fence, beef-mad and howling. He made them wait while he went to the barn for his fishing gear. When he returned he nudged the meat toward them. It was barely enough to keep the dogs alive. They lunged at it, ripped it, as he picked up the switch that was hooked to the fence and beat them. He whipped them as they ate, only as they ate. So they hurried.

When João disappeared into the bamboo, Vó opened the screen door, patting the hinges as though that would hush the squeak. "Quickly," she said. Already, at 7 A.M. in the San Joaquin Valley, the temperature was eighty degrees and climbing, the heat making the dirt too hot to stand on in bare feet. Because of the hot earth, my grandmother wore slippers—black wide-wale corduroy that she shuffled through the dust. Her knees were starting to bother her.

I carried a bucket with chuck scraps. Vó held an enameled tin cup half full of the strong coffee she took with her every morning as she fed the dogs and watered her kale and turnips and coriander. She had loquat and walnut trees, too, and flowers—peonies and lilacs. I gave my avó the bucket, then stood guard under the fig tree. Nearing the pen, she pulled out the chuck and dropped it by the gate. She used her foot to sweep it under, fast, before the dogs made too much noise. The animals snatched the beef inside their slack-flabby jowls and gnashed with their rotting teeth, peering at us with their awful seeping eyes. Sly. Snarling. They did not snarl at my grandfather.

When Sylvia told me she was evicting me, I had said, "Am I that bad?"

She had taken my face in her hands, patted my cheeks, and said, "Oh my poor, needy baby." Nothing more.

I took my avó's hand, the skin worn thin and soft. "C'mon." She glanced at the pen. "Let's get out of here."

Often that summer, I'd fish with my grandfather. He always brought a bottle he'd filled with Vó's wine. He'd give me a few slugs of wine. I'd grin, staring at mud swirl in the river, ignoring the tugs on my line. One day he said, "You will take over the chore of mine that is feeding the dogs."

"You wouldn't make me do something I couldn't stand to do."

He batted at the air, waving me away as he did when he felt I pestered him. "I would. You are too much like Sylvia. Soft. But I have the faith. I can fix you."

Sylvia had given up all hope of fixing me. "I give up," she'd said after I had curled my tongue for the altar boy during communion. He was seventeen, and my friends and I all had crushes on him. It was this altar boy's job to hold the paten beneath my chin to catch the wine-soaked host, should I drop it. The curl had been for his benefit. I'd looked straight at him, not the priest holding the wafer. I'd seen him, the altar boy, start to smile. The priest had not looked amused, though he was young and progressive. He just took the wafer and tapped my tongue so I'd flatten it.

"What is your trouble?" Sylvia asked me that evening, when I came out on the patio to grab some chips and onion dip from their cock-tail tray.

Smoothing dip into the grooves of the chip, I said, "I'm not the troubled one here."

"Gus?" Sylvia had turned to her husband for help. "I cannot deal with this." She held up her hand to ward off even the idea of me. "Handle her."

"Easy now, Sylvia," Gus said.

I turned to my mother, took her highball glass from her, and said, "No, *you* handle me. *You* do it. It's *your* job."

"Some job," she said. "Where's my pension. Where's my drink?"

"This is not an attractive side of you, Sylvia," Gus said.

"No?" Sylvia snatched the bowl of dip from my reach. "Should I douse myself with your favorite pisswater, Eau de Ex-Mrs. Gus Souza, to regain my allure?"

"Take that back, Sylvia," I said. "Take it back about the job or I keep the drink."

"Okay, okay," she said. "Now give me the drink or I'll keep the dip."

"Holy hell, Sylvia," Gus said. "Throw the damned stuff out if it bothers you so much."

My grandfather mentioned his plans for me and the dogs, but he never implemented them. I think he enjoyed the tension he was building. We continued to fish, to drink the sweet wine.

My avó's wine was far more potent than the stuff in screw-cap bottles that my friends and I conned people into buying for us. We stood in the liquor-store parking lot, allowances ready, waiting for someone who looked like they might take our money and get us some wine. They were usually men, our buyers, in their twenties— salesmen who worked from their mid-sized four doors and stayed at the motel down the road from the liquor store. Sometimes, after coming back across the gravel lot with the paper bag of our wine, they'd ask my friends and me to have a drink with them.

If there was no movie to see or party to crash, we went along and sat in their cars on woven plastic seat protectors, sipping peach or apple or strawberry wine, usually from expandable travel cups, listening to stories about regional sales. It made me feel that I was going places, sitting in those cars, looking at the windshield visors packed with maps of the Gold Country, Yosemite, the Bay Area.

I felt that sense of moving toward something when I fished with my grandfather on the riverbank, watching the water slog to the Pacific. He looked at the river the way those salesmen looked at the highway—longing, edgy, apart from all of it.

Stuffing pieces of cheese loaf onto my fishing hook, I made João tell me about São Miguel, the island in the Azores where he'd been born. "A carton of eggs was twenty dollars," he told me. "Still, I have not felt like who I am since I left."

Sometimes, when I was at home and had to get out and my friends were busy, I went by myself to beg drinks. One night, my legs sticking to the vinyl seat of a Nova, sipping peach wine from a thermos cap, the windows open to the air, heavy with almond blossoms and trapped exhaust, I sat with a salesman whose hair was sweet with Butch Wax.

He told me about his favorite parts of the state. He loved the red-wood tree you could drive a car through. He couldn't get over The House of Mystery, the home with stairs leading to nowhere and doors opening into the sky because the owner's dead husband told her she'd die if she stopped building. "Keep building," he wailed to her from beyond the grave.

During a monologue about the ghost town of Columbia, he started kissing me, and I, buzzed from the wine, envisioning freewheeling down Highway 49, kissed back. He tasted of peach wine and cigarettes and taco sauce. "Whew boy," I said. He played my spine with the pads of his fingers, distracted. When he reached inside the buttons of my blouse, his touch was sly and lazy, not like the timid scoutings of the guys I went out with. My face buzzed, as if it had fallen asleep. He kept sneaking inside my blouse and I kept moving his hand, taking longer each time. The last time I reached for his fingers, he batted mine away.

"Hey," I pushed him back. "Cut it out."

A bead of Butch Wax dripped from his bristled hairline.

"Look," I tried to lighten things. "There's nothing there anyway." I pulled a map from the visor, ran my fingers across the flat paper surface. "You may as well have at this."

He nodded toward my fingers, still smoothing the map. "It seems to work for you." I stilled them. He lifted my hand and took the map from me. "Will you stay and watch?" He opened the map once.

It took me a minute. "Uh, no." I pushed at the door handle, pushed again. "Thanks, though." I jumped out of the car, and ran without looking back for the lights of the liquor store, where I called Gus to pick me up. For a minute, in the Nova, I'd felt as if I could break free, move on someday, maybe get my own four-door and product line. But in the liquor store, all I could do was hover by the cashier and watch for Gus to take me back to the house I'd escaped from earlier that night.

"I love watching it, the river," João told me one afternoon as we fished. We sat halfway down the bank, shaded by oak, leaning forward on our poles. I watched the water, swift, muddy—its flow interrupted here and there by whirlpools, sucking the water toward the bottom.

"I never felt the hope so much as when I got on the boat for this country," he said. He sighed. "You have never seen a thing so beautiful as São Miguel," he said. It was the island where he'd been born.

"Tomorrow," he told me, "you start with the dogs. No more protests."

"I won't," I told him.

"What I say, you do. Where else you live, *neh?*"

We said nothing else while we fished, nor as we walked up the bank. With me, building tension was what he relished most. It had never gone further. He left me at the dog pen, while he put away the fishing gear. Facing the dog pen, my back to him, I waited until I heard him closing the barn doors behind him, heard him click the padlock, felt him approaching me, his floppy hat pushed back on his head, work trousers hanging low on his time-flattened ass, as he walked toward the pen, spitting tobacco from the face that had done my avó in when she was a girl in the Azores.

Maybe it was seeing my avó watching from the bathroom window that caused me to do it. The glimpse, from behind the terry-cloth curtain, of her strong nose and her steely hair, that caused me to take the loaf of processed cheese from my basket, drop it to the ground, and kick it under the wire.

My foot never returned to the ground.

With one swipe of his boot, my grandfather kicked the other foot out from under me, landing me flat on my back in the dirt. I held my eyes wide open. I would not cry. "Hey," I said. This was behavior he reserved for his children. "It's me."

"I know who you are," he said. "You leave my dogs."

"I won't let you starve them."

"In my house," he said. "I make the rules." He reached out his hand to help me up. "Come, Marva."

An apology. Maybe he didn't want to scare me off the way he had his daughters, whipping them with his belt, refusing to speak to their fiancés (he wanted arranged marriages) on his property, and when they crossed him, refusing to speak to them as though they were dead to him.

Still, I waved him away. Eye level with the dogs' mouths, I cringed as they ripped into the cheese, then fought to chew through the gummy loaf. They yelped with the difficulty of trying to swallow the food that glued their teeth together. I heard Vó yelling from the house, shuffling toward the pen.

"Leave her, old man," she said, scuttling toward us on her stiff legs. "And wash yourself for dinner."

The old man had caught me with his dogs once before, and he hadn't done anything. I was seven. The dogs were different ones, young and not yet mean, and I thought they were lonely so I put one of the new kittens in the pen. One of the dogs grabbed the kitten in his mouth and shook it until its neck snapped. I screamed. My grandfather ran over. "Jesus," he said, pronouncing it *JeZuej*. "It is a mistake, *leãozinha*. Only that."

My grandfather and I buried the kitten down by the river. We sang Fados in Portuguese, words I didn't know but tried to fake in kind of a low, lisping chant. After the funeral, he took me out and let me shoot his twenty-two rifle. He stood behind me and held his right hand over mine. His left hand he placed between my shoulder and the butt of the gun so I wouldn't bruise from the slight kick.

During dinner, not an hour after he'd kicked my feet out from under me, the old man kept his head to his soup. I sat across from him with a clear view of my avó at the stove. She cut the sausage right on the bag she used to drain it, then put the slices onto an oval serving dish, the one with the faint line through the corner where a chip had been re-glued. The old man reached for the potato salad that Vó and I had made with fresh peas, home-pressed olive oil, and mint. He held his soup plate out to his wife, who stood by the stove. He cleared his throat, grunted. Four times before she filled his plate.

I couldn't eat. I kept seeing the dogs ripping into the cheese, eyes wild, bodies slouched low to the dirt in anticipation of the whip. I played with my soup, spooning the turnip greens, thyme leaves, the potatoes—dropping them back into my bowl.

"They will be very sick, the dogs, from all the food you gave for them," he said.

I looked at Vó, who shook her head.

"What?" I asked.

"Come here, *leãozinha*." João wiped soup from his lip. "Lean closer, let me show you where the mouse stole my tooth."

"I don't want to," I said, though I didn't want to fight with him.

He leaned toward me, opened his mouth, and stuck his finger into the corner to pull back the skin. There was a hole where a tooth had been, a hole he showed me whenever he felt like teasing me with the mouse story. It was rough skinned and red like the rest of his gums, only it puckered around the void where his tooth had been. A small piece of turnip green was stuck in the hole, and it clung to his tongue by a thin band of spit.

He watched me scrutinizing him. "Doesn't she look just like Sylvia?" he asked.

Vó said nothing.

"Old woman?"

Vó turned from the stove. She would not sit. She never sat down with us, but ate goat cheese and loquats in her garden, brushing loose strands of hair from her face between bites, chewing slowly, alone and content. "Understand this thing, you whatever-you-are, Marva does not pay to you for the sins of Sylvia."

He waved his wife away, looked from his wife to me, watching.

Vó turned back to the stove, stirring the fava beans she was cooking with tomatoes and onion. As she cooked, she watched João, banging the stove lids to warn him away. She dipped her ladle into the bean pot and poured the stew over the sausage. He took a couple pieces of the perch she'd fried with cornmeal, then spooned on the sauce of home-cured green olives, roasted walnuts, and fresh coriander. He added fresh sliced tomatoes to his plate and home-pickled banana peppers, hot and garlicky. Sawing a piece of bread from the loaf she'd just pulled from the oven, he smeared it with butter. Dessert was set up on the sideboard—loquat cream custard and a dish of walnuts with a crystallized sherry crust. Every day he ate like this.

"Finish your soup, Marva," he said.

Vó rattled the pan lid.

He reached for the sausage. "Try some, Marva, move your soup bowl, so I can put some on your plate."

I batted his hand away, trying to joke, to get things back to the way they had been when I was younger. "Hey."

"You have the hunger. I know. Come on now, move your plate over here."

I tapped my foot against the chair rung.

"Stop it," he said.

"I can't."

"You will break the chair."

"No I won't."

He used his index finger to prod the hand that held my fork, all the time watching for my avó's reaction. "You can't eat what I eat?"

I glared at him.

Vó was behind me. Her fingers gripped my shoulders.

"You need to eat," he said.

"I need a cigarette."

He set down the sausage, reached into his shirt pocket, and got a cigarette for me. He lit it with his thank-you lighter from the gas station.

He spooned the beans onto his plate. Watching us both, he held the spoon over mine. I spread my free hand over my dish, but he grabbed my wrist and moved my hand firmly away.

I leaned forward, and, with my eyes on his bloodshot ones, lowered the ember of my cigarette to the tablecloth, dissolving the yellow calico oilcloth as it burned. I looked right at him. Watch out, I thought. I pointed to my head. "I won't disappear like Sylvia." I didn't put my cloth napkin on the burn, or pour my glass of water on it, or even take my cigarette away, but watched the hole grow wider and blacker.

Vó was no longer gripping my shoulders. She placed her hands on my head and pulled my head back against her.

"No dogs," Vó said.

"No dogs." He put down the serving fork, looked at me, then smiled, a big wide grin. "There is no need."

I looked at him closely, trying to find the man I'd known five weeks before, so I could smile back. But I couldn't, not then.

I felt my avó's smooth cotton dress on the back of my neck, the worn leather of her belt and the pressed lace handkerchief she tucked into it, and the rosaries she hung from it. Then Vó let go. My head spun for a minute. All I could think of was that I had just ruined what was one of Vó's favorite tablecloths. I dabbed water on the burn, unable to rise from the table.

After my grandfather died—coughing and wheezing in the middle of the night, from pneumonia, they said—sometime later that year, a few months after I went back to live with my mother and stepfather, Vó pushed the wheelbarrow from the house to the river, hauling load after load of her husband's shirts and fishing equipment, dumping them into the current. As she pushed, her slippers flopped on the dirt path, and she muttered, "Goddamn you," and, "Son of a bitch. You son of a bitch," until all traces of him were gone.

But before that, the night the dogs feasted on the cheese loaf, Vó and I did the dishes as we had done every night of the summer. The old man walked by and tugged at my apron string in greeting before he went out to the shed to pour himself a cup of wine from the barrel. He sat on the bench under the oak tree and killed time by flattening ants with his fly swatter, smashing them as they crawled across the dirt.

When Vó and I went out to drink our iced tea, as we did every night, in the front seat of the old Plymouth, the old man sat looking at us. He seemed so sad, his jaw slack, as though he wanted to be let off the hook. I called for him to sit with us. I didn't see my grandmother's face behind me, but it couldn't have been welcoming because he waved us both away and walked past the gate without a word and then down to the river.

Vó set her glass on the floor and held my face, turning it from side to side. She combed my hair back with her fingers, tried to fix it in place with pins from her own hair. "It will not stay down," she laughed.

"Did you used to comb my mother's hair like this?"

"Nobody could touch the head of that girl." She said it with affection.

We couldn't have gone anywhere that night in the car. Though João let me drive without a license, my grandmother would not. She had certain things that she was stubborn about. And João had parked the car with the front end to the shed so his wife would have had to reverse it to go anywhere. She did not drive in reverse.

"I don't want to be like him or Sylvia or my father."

"We are not so different," she said. "Any of us. You will do fine. I know this."

I wanted to know things as she did. Tightening my grip on the wheel, I stared at the roughened wood, the lined grain, interrupted by knots where the limbs had once been, stared ahead as she did, at what I didn't know, into the future perhaps, at some exit she saw in the shed wall in front of us, some path through the whorls or between the planks.

My mom shows her little girl how to rock. 1978.

Michelle Coppedge has been writing poetry, fiction, and various scribblings since at least the age of seven. Born in Virginia, she grew up in Charlotte, North Carolina, graduated from the University of North Carolina at Chapel Hill, and currently lives, works, and plays in Carrboro, North Carolina. Her work has been published in *Cellar Door, Shakespeare's Sister,* and *Dancing on the Moon.* When not writing, she often heads for the mountains or the coast, plays the flute, or curls up in a coffee-shop with a book in front of her face. Michelle is very excited about her first appearance in *Glimmer Train.*

THE DRESS

Michelle Coppedge

Michelle Coppedge

Below the skin of your face, the years
Of babies crying, your husband's silence—

Your own infolding. I have grown
Up seeing the battle inside you.

We laugh just alike. We cry just
Alike. I want you always to find me

Funny—the child who postured
In your wedding dress, danced

Importantly in its billows and gapes. Grown,
I can no longer close around me its fabric,

That remnant of the day when everything before
You could still be perfect. I wonder,

Where is the moment when what
Is perfect shifts from future to past?

You want me not to break stride, not
To take the wrong step. I'm careful that

Michelle Coppedge

My feet miss your tracks. Ahead of me, you hurry,
Eyes down to the path, not looking back

At what you think is too late. Mother,
You are in me, in my cold sleeplessness,

My belly laughter.
          Tonight, I stand behind

You in the kitchen, drying the dishes you
Scrub clean. On your plates, there is food

You made that they did not eat.
I notice how round your shoulders are,

How small—
          Then you spin around,

Suds sprouting from your chin as you dab
A silly beard on me. We are goofy twins,

And I find I cannot say what I want to: *There*
Is your life, which is not mine, and here is my life,

Which is not yours.

POETRY OPEN WINNERS

1ST PLACE

Michelle Coppedge receives $500 for "The Dress."

Coppedge's bio is on page 198 preceding her poem.

2ND PLACE

Gillian Devereux for "What We See under Water."

Gillian Devereux received her MFA in Poetry from Old Dominion University. In 2003, she served as Artist in Residence at Buena Vista University in Storm Lake, Iowa. Her poems have appeared in the *New Journal* and the *Powhatan Review*.

3RD PLACE

Ariana-Sophia Kartsonis for "Charm for the Drowned Boy."

Ariana-Sophia Kartsonis currently lives and works in Cincinnati. Her work is forthcoming in *Hotel Amerika* and *Glimmer Train*.

*We invite you to visit **www.glimmertrain.com** to see a list of the top twenty-five winners and finalists. We thank all entrants for sending in their work.*

*I think I had outgrown the dress
when Mother took this picture.*

Lori Ann Stephens earned her MA in Studies in Literature at the University of Texas at Dallas, where she is completing her PhD in Humanities. She currently teaches literature and writing courses at Richland Community College and at UT Dallas, and lives in Richardson with her son, Trevor.

WE CRY FOR US

Lori Ann Stephens

for Hervé Abdi

I

When I was four, I found God under our organ.

Tuesday, and Mother ties her black hair up in the lime green scarf and opens up every door in the house. Bedroom doors, closet doors, bathroom doors, cabinets, cupboards, linen, laundry doors. A house never has so many doors until they're all open. Tuesday, and she props open every door and makes our house a giant maze. A mouse maze, because whoever decorated the house before we moved there didn't know anything about hanging doors and put the doors on backwards. They all open into the hallways and make a labyrinth. I play the little white mouse, running the maze while Mother wraps her hand up in a dust cloth, like a white boxing glove, and wipes down the doors.

"I'm a mouse," I say and run past Mother. I weave around the doors, a pale, underweight mouse with pigtails.

"*Flaca*, you are not a mouse, you are a monkey," Mother sings. "Mice, they are quiet. They don't move for hours, find good place to hide. And they say nothing. So silent, the baby cannot hear them. The angels, they sing for the little mice. Do you hear when they sing?"

Her eyes are large black pools. I want to swim in them.

"No," I say, and she looks away, back at a curved line of dust on the door.

"They do not come when you are knocking the doors to the king-dom come. The angels, they sing to quiet little mice, not sing to the monkeys."

I search for the hiding place, under the end table, in the hamper, behind Father's green-striped chair. I want to hear the angels sing. Mother wipes down the doors. Across the top ledge, around the door-knob, her finger slides across the underside that even mice cannot see. She cleans for my baby brother, Paul, who has asthma.

I watched him turn blue in his crib on my fourth birthday. I stood with my feet wedged between the spindles of the crib, my hands on the rim, my chin on my hands, eyes on his face, his translucent skin turning blue, then a beautiful violet. His skin smelled like fresh milk. Mother slapped my legs with a dishcloth and I jumped down. Move, *Flaca*. Don't climb on the crib like a monkey. Then she saw Paul's violet eyelids and swooped him up like a great hawk, and we all flew to the hospital. Three days later, Mother came home with Paul in one arm and a paper sack full of long dust rags in the other.

I have a good memory. Some people can't remember when they were four. I remember blue fire in a globe when I was one.

Mother came home with Paul on a Tuesday, and from that day on, every Tuesday Mother tied up her long black hair, opened all the doors in the house, and bound up her fist in a damp rag to hunt for dust. I hunted for angels.

I ask Mother again, again, again, when the angels will sing. She heaves a sigh and says she'll make them start singing, mouse or no. She pulls out her old shoebox of tapes, slides one in the organ, and turns the volume up so loud I feel the brown burlap speakers pulse under my arm. Under the organ, behind the bench, my legs draped over the long cherrywood foot pedals. A miracle place, where I cup my hands over my ears and squeeze my eyes tight and wish for miracles, for baby Paul to breathe again and for Mother to swing me up in the air, her feet under my belly, and make me a bird again. A quiet place, so quiet I can hear my nose whistle during the static silence between

204

hymns, but so loud I hear the pulsing, roaring shouts of angels who spread their wings over me, sing to me, hide me away from Paul, from dust and violet and black pools I'm afraid to wade in.

While Mother sweeps up clumps of dried dirt and yellow grass in the kitchen, sloshes water across the floor, scratches muck off the tile with her fingernail, and gently wipes the tops and bottoms of each hibiscus leaf, I press my ears to the fabric and listen to angels singing through scratchy burlap right into my ear and down to my stomach.

The angels live in God's throat, and He speaks to me through the organ. Every Tuesday I crawl under the keys, my head pressed to the fabric, letting God's voice shoot down through my legs. The vibrations echo down through my arms to my fingertips, until my whole body quivers with music. *Leaning, leaning, leaning on the everlasting arms.* I am four, and God moves in me like butterflies.

Mother didn't always go to the church. She wasn't always a Christian. Father met her in Colombia while he was hammering nails into two-by-fours in a build-a-thon church-raising mission in a jungle clearing. He flew to Colombia with fifteen men and raised three churches in three weeks. Mother brought the workers *jugo de lulo.* Fifteen men swirled and sniffed their juice except Father, who drank Mother's lulo juice like a bear and smiled at her from the roof beam. She had wild black hair tied back from her face, and teeth so white Father said an angel was hiding under her tongue. He called her Angelina, although it wasn't her name, and held her hand under the blessed beams of the first church service.

So Mother buttoned up the white satin *traje de novia* embroidered in bougainvillea, told her own mama, No, the witch doctor cannot come to the ceremony, and walked head-high down the aisle.

Grandmother sobbed, "*Pobrecita mi hijita,*" because Mother married on Sunday the seventh. *Domingo 7 ni te cases ni te embarques.* I was not supposed to know this, but I heard Mother tell the witch doctor over smoking leaves. Caught words and phrases I hid behind my knees until I grew old enough to understand them.

Grandmother gave a piece of her soul to the Devil that day. The witch doctor wasn't invited, still the Devil held fast to one of Mother's heels, even after the baptismal water dripped down the tips of her hair, even after she sprinkled herbs for good luck over her satin wedding gown.

Do you promise to love and obey God the Father and Jesus the Son? *Si.* Do you promise to honor your husband? *Si.*

"*Pobrecita mi hijita, te casaste con este gringo,*" Grandmother cried.

Do you promise to leave behind the idols of your youth for the one and only true God? *Si.* In the name of the Father, the Son, and the Holy Spirit. I remember it even before I was born.

Six years later, six dry years after she'd flown away from Colombia to my father's home in America, she dragged me off the public bus and into the streets where newspapers and plastic cups and hotdog wrappers swirled in the air. This was the street Father never knew about. Wednesdays, when Mother's lungs failed and she cried to Father she couldn't drag herself to church, we walked the street of endless brick row houses lined with bottomless iron ladders and windows like small prisons. Cells for the wicked old women who peeked out their dingy curtains.

The hideous woman behind the green door was on this street because she chopped off children's ears when they didn't listen to her. And the man who smoked two cigars on the stoop next door had been waiting two hundred years for his wife, smoking her cigar so it would be hot when she finally returned. A little boy my size had wheels on his shoes, and kept falling on his bleeding knees. The tales in my head gave me goosepimples, and I gripped Mother's hand. The sky here was darker and the clouds hung lower than on the street where I lived. Even at five, I knew the people were wicked in this part of town because of the prison bar windows, and because men in hats sat on porch stoops smoking cigarettes, carefully guarding the people inside.

Wednesday, and we plodded to the witch doctor.

"You not tell your father, or Paul be cursed, *Flaca.*" Mother carried Paul on her hip and tied a long cloth sling over her shoulder to support him. His legs dangled past her thighs, limp and brown like *sancocho de gallina.* Paul was sick again, blue in the morning and violet at night. What the church couldn't do for Paul on Sundays, the witch doctor tried to cure on Wednesdays.

The witch doctor was a woman married to an old chemistry professor. He answered the door in a cooking apron. His thick glasses made a deep dent in his nose, and he offered us a toothy smile and a ladle of warm, thick liquid he'd been stirring on the stove. His lips were pink and swollen like pig tongues.

His wife, the witch doctor, wore long dresses that rustled like the old cornhusks Mother strung together and hung in the kitchen window. Her long fingers dangled in the air like spider legs, and when she reached out to Mother, I wanted both to pull Mother away from the woman and to take her spidery hands into my own to examine them. I was afraid for Mother and curious about the witch doctor at the same time. Do you see her hands, Mother? Don't let them crawl all over the baby.

Their house was the brick row house at the end of the street. I wondered what crime they'd committed, who they were hiding from, why the professor had walnuts for knuckles.

Mother sat with the witch doctor under the weeping willow, Paul wrapped around her waist, his head resting on her breast above her heart. I wasn't allowed to hear the fortune, so I sat on the stairs and tried to read their lips, tried to hear their whispers singing. I tried to imagine the beating, rhythmic sound in her breast. The professor stirred chicken hearts on the kitchen stove, but the odor in the house smelled of attic dust, of linseed oil, cat hair, and boxes of clothes opened after years of heat and rain.

"Try this, Rebecka," the professor said. He lifted the spoon and held it over his cupped hand. I didn't like the smell, didn't like the thought of small rubbery hearts rolling on my tongue. But Father told me never say no to an adult, don't be rude, Rebecka. I looked back at Mother, she would rescue me, but I only saw a piece of her skirt as she closed the screen door to the back porch steps. I turned back to the professor and he held the spoon of broth in front of me.

"Taste," he said. I couldn't say yes, but no was forbidden. So I nodded, my eyes filling with tears and my chin trembling. I nodded yes, but squeezed my lips together. I hate Paul for bringing us here, I thought, and my eyes burned as my tears fell.

The professor's lips peeled back over his big teeth and he laughed. He rubbed his round belly with his free hand, making small circles on the apron. He patted my head. "Okay," he said, and laughed again. "You don't like my cooking? I have a caramel you will definitely like."

I wait on their back porch, chewing caramel, and scratch white hearts into the wood with a piece of limestone. Mother never smokes a cigar at home, but she does at the witch doctor's. We buy a cigar on the way and mother stuffs it deep into her purse. She sits on the stone bench with the witch doctor and they talk. One of Mother's hands moves in the air like a moth, the other strokes Paul's black, curly hair. I can smell his skin, like fresh yeast, all the way from the porch. The witch doctor puffs on the cigar and waits, watching the red fire glow at the end. She taps the ashes and puffs again. Her finger points and circles the glowing ash, then she hands the cigar to Mother. Mother puffs and sucks until the end glows like the ring around a blood moon. They talk again in low whispers. The smoke swirls above Paul's head like a white halo. The witch doctor takes Paul's hand, small and doughy like bread balls Mother gives me to knead. The women puff and wait and watch the cigar ash grow longer and longer and longer, until bits of white ash float up and away like dust on angel wings. They smile at each other and laugh softly.

"*Tengo que hacer una limpia*," Mother whispers as we climb the green bus that takes us home. "*Una limpia.*"

"What's that?" I ask. Mother taps my nose.

"You not tell Father about these place, okay? Is a secret." She tickles my neck.

The bus moves, and Mother sings a song about the girl who lives on the moon, the girl who has no father or mother and cries alone.

Most Wednesdays were not full of smoke and ash and red brick row houses. Most Wednesdays, Father got sick of Mother being sick, and he told her if she was going to die, she might as well be in church and save him the extra trip. Tuesday night, she'd sniff and pull the blanket stitched with green ivy up under her chin and whimper about her lungs aching from all the dust stirred up from Tuesday's cleaning. "What's good enough for Lazarus and Jarius's girl and Jesus is good enough for you," he told her.

Mother woke me from muddy afternoon dreams and pulled a dress over my head. Slipped on white socks with the white-lace frill and my black patent-leather shoes, and pulled me out the front door. Father waiting in the station wagon, always checking his watch, engine humming, I'd wake up in the car by rubbing the hard grit of sleep out of my eyes. I noticed the white lace on my ankles. Lace-trimmed socks were for babies, not seven year olds, so I tucked the fringe under when Mother wasn't looking and gave the lace trim the evil eye so it would shrivel up and fall off. By the time we parked the car in front of the big white cross, the sun was orange and low and I was ready to skip or play hopscotch or chase the butterflies in the empty lot beside the church. I looked at the green grass bending, beckoning to me as Father whisked me up the steps and into the sanctuary.

The sanctuary had cherry-wood pews and plush red carpet, red tapestries on the walls where Jesus was still hanging on the cross, where blood still drizzled down his cheeks, so that if the pastor forgot to mention the blood of the lamb (which he rarely did), the room whispered it for him. I thought the church was gloomy, didn't like hearing about killing lambs and blood all the time. I kept confusing sanctuary with cemetery.

Father wouldn't let me lie down on the pews like the Turner children did. The six of them took up a whole pew with their legs sprawled out. I had to sit with my hands in my lap and my legs crossed at the ankles. Father's back was straight as a tree, and his head nodded like swaying mimosas when the pastor said something wise.

If my feet started swinging, Father gave me the look. Then I imagined my legs were nailed to the pews so I'd be allowed to hold Paul when it was time. Swinging legs were rude. I am not a rude girl like Bethany, I thought. Bethany didn't share her suckers with me after

Sunday School. She would tell me to learn the Bible verses and earn my own suckers. I knew the words, but I kept confusing the books and chapters and verses. She would stick her orange tongue out at me and slowly lick the orb. When my legs tingled, I stuck them out straight and looked at the hairs on my knees. I pulled the tiny hairs until my skin hurt to wake up my legs.

Paul was three, but he was still small like a Rubby-Dub Baby. The pastor called the sick and the sinners to the bench almost every Wednesday, so I knew I'd get to hold Paul when Father led Mother to the front of the church. Paul spoke little sentences I only understood sometimes, but his favorite phrase he saved for church.

"Come to the Lord, all who are weak and weary," the pastor beckoned.

"Oh, no," Paul said, as though a balloon had popped. Mother placed Paul on my lap.

"Come to the feast of forgiveness."

"Oh, no!" Paul's hands were on his hollow cheeks, his mouth and eyes like three little Os. Father took Mother's hand and they joined the river of people trickling to the front.

"The Comforter's table. He's calling you with that still, small voice."

"Oh, no! Oh, no! Oh, nooo!" Paul smiled at the sound of his own voice.

I bounced my knees and tickled his stomach. He clapped his hands and shrieked. I looked at Father, who was already shaking his head at me while placing his hands on an old woman's white head. He was praying to God with his mouth and speaking to me with his eyes at the same time, which only increased my amazement with my father.

The people at the church knew Father was particularly close to Jesus. They gathered around him at prayer time so his hands landed on their heads even when his eyes were closed. They felt a current, they said, a supernatural current in his fingers that made their knees bend like saplings. Standing up at the sinner's bench, he towered over the other church members, and he seemed very far from me. His arms outstretched, he looked like Jesus, like Noah on the ark, like the little wooden doll that dangled on twine around the witch doctor's neck. Did it hurt when the people fell backwards, I wondered. Did it hurt when the electricity flew from his fingernails? I slipped my hand in his after the service and waited for the small shock to make me fall backwards, but I only felt skin, cool and dry and comfortable.

Except for when Father was making the congregation faint, church wasn't fun like my friend Lucy's church. She was a Catholic. I went with her one Sunday, and we stood up and sat down and stood up and sat down. The priest kept everyone exercising. At my church, we sat in the pews and listened to sermons about blood and fornication and multitudes while I itched and waited for the call for the sick and sinners.

After church was Special Time with Father. My father had the idea when I was five and Paul's skin first turned blue. While Mother took Paul home and sat rocking him, his little pursed lips at her warm breast, and him listening to her steady heartbeat, a still mouse, I was in the Luby's cafeteria reciting Bible verses. Not even Bible verses from Sunday school, but *extra* Bible verses that Father hand-picked himself. I wanted to be next to Mother, small again and wrapped in a baby blanket. I wanted my skin to smell like fresh milk and feel like bread dough. I held my breath and tried to turn blue. My head pounded and my cheeks burned, but I wanted to be violet so I could lay my head on Mother's breast and feel her hands stroking my brown hair. Father looked over his newspaper and told me to stop playing.

"Who loves you, baby?" he says. He holds his coffee cup to his lips, his newspaper folded on the table.

"Jesus." I stuff a large piece of angel-food cake in my mouth and chew.

"*Ephesians* 6:1." He leans over to me as though he's going to kiss me. I close my eyes and wait, but nothing. I open them again, and he's staring at me like an eagle.

" 'Children...,' " Father draws out the word like thick milk.

" 'Obey your parents in the Lord, for this is right.' *Ephesians* 6:1." I smash the cake with the tines of my fork. They make thin yellow sponge rows.

"Right," he says. He sips his coffee and opens his black Bible. "And what will God do for you when you obey your parents?"

People look at Father. I feel their eyes on me, smiling eyes, sad eyes, wide plate-eyes, and I don't feel like a mouse at all. I feel like a monkey.

I scratch my head and push mashed cake into my lower-lip pocket. My lip juts out and the cake feels cool on my teeth. "I'm a monkey."

"You are *not* a monkey. You're a child of God, and everything you say will be *God* speaking because *God* is inside you."

I look at the lady behind Father. She shakes her head. Father taps his Bible.

"Answer me, Rebecka. What will God do for you when you obey your parents?"

"I'll live a long time." I say it loudly so the lady will hear and stop shaking her head. I stuff another piece of cake into my mouth.

Father nods his head. "That's right, baby. Who loves you?"

"Jesus."

"And who will protect you?"

"Jesus." I think about my baby brother. "Why doesn't Jesus protect Paul?"

Father sucks in a big breath and makes whistles with his nostrils. He frowns and looks at the Bible page open on the table. "Can you say, 'Greater is He who is in me than he who is in the world'?"

"I don't think so."

"Go ahead. 'Greater is He…'"

I recited every verse. Every Sunday, every Special Time, every word. Five verses every Wednesday, in addition to the ones I'd learned the previous week. Before I got home, I'd have *thee*s and *thou*s and waltzing hotdog wrappers and smoking cigars churning in my brain like meringue, fluffy and melting at the same time. I went to bed, the angel-food cake bubbling in my stomach. I had to squeeze my throat to keep it all down.

Poor Mother. The Devil whispered to her at night. She woke, her nightgown soaked through with sweat, and tiptoed into our room. Kissed me on the forehead. Kissed baby Paul on his blue hand, then pulled the wet gown off over her head and stood naked, looking at the moon through our window. She thought I was sleeping, and she said a prayer in Spanish. *Protege mi hijo.* Mother never spoke to us in Spanish—only a few words here or there—but I knew her prayers weren't to the God Father prayed to. *Diablo.* I watched her. *Diablo,* she cried, and her sweat glistened and slipped down the curve of her back.

II

Our street didn't have red brick row houses. Our tract-house duplexes lined up like giant frogs, two wide-eyed windows in front, and two garages that flanked the sides like hunched legs. Most of the houses in our neighborhood looked alike. My house was the only one on the block with a red door, which was something to brag about to other children on our street. But when Helen Stein told all the block children the *sun* slept in her house, and we all sat on my porch and watched the orange bubble slip right down her chimney, everyone laughed and agreed, including me, that Helen's house had a special blessing.

Helen Stein had a crystal bead bracelet, a jumbo plastic pool, a permanent hair-do with a thousand curls, and a goat named Reuben in the backyard. Mother said goats were bad luck. An evil omen. Paul turned blue the day after Helen Stein's family moved in across the street, which made Mother shake her head and say, "Why I am always right about these things?" I wasn't allowed to play in Helen's house, and if I played too long in their front yard, I had to rinse the spirits off my skin with the yard hose before coming into our house.

The lonely widow who lived next door in Helen's duplex gave Helen and me cookies and rolls if we'd come over and visit her for a few minutes. If she didn't have cookies or rolls, she'd give us a spoonful of whipped cream or carrot sticks dipped in peanut butter. We would have visited her even if she gave us cotton to suck on, her stories were so good.

The widow told us about the people in Babahoyo who had no bank one hundred years ago. They placed their coins and gold and jewelry in a pot and buried the pot behind their houses.

"People did that everywhere. Probably even on this street," Helen said.

"Maybe," the widow said. Then she leaned over and whispered. "But when someone in Babahoyo died, if you went into his garden at night, a bright light from the sky would shine right down on the spot where the treasure was buried." The widow and Helen and I had the same idea at that moment. We followed the widow to her old shed, which she hadn't opened since her husband had died, and the rust on the door floated down like red flakes of rain. She handed us two garden shovels and gave us the key to the shed, since she never bothered with tools anymore.

"And when you're not looking for treasure, you can plant these flowers here in the garden. If you find the time." She stepped around a dozen cartons of flowers we hadn't noticed on the way to the shed.

Helen and I climbed into every backyard on the street that summer after the fireflies stopped glowing. While Father was out of town getting jobs for immigrants, and Mother sat beside Paul, watching him breathe in his sleep, I was writing down a wish list for the treasure we'd find. Glow-in-the-dark shoelaces. Blueberry-flavored lip gloss. Hot pink Girl Power bike with silver tassels and basket. Helen held the shovels while I climbed over the wire fence and unlocked the gate. Then both of us crawled on our knees across the dark garden until we found a comfortable place to wait for the light to illuminate the spot where one hundred years ago someone buried silver spoons or gold necklaces. We watched five baby owls learn to fly and we found a Frisbee half buried behind a tree. We collected two quartz rocks, a turtle shell and a dog's tooth, but there was no other night treasure.

In the cool mornings before the heat set in, we planted the zinnias and verbena in the widow's garden. Then Helen and I climbed up the widow's orange tree that overlooked Helen's backyard so I could watch Reuben. We sucked the juice out of the orange and threw the soggy flesh down to the goat. Helen told me about her uncle, Rebbe Yosef, who was kicked out of his synagogue for having an affair with the Rabbi's wife, and I told Helen about Juan's fake eyeball, about Ivonne and Maria and other children on our street.

Maria had a cousin with a shrunken head. His tiny head might have been only a little small for a six-year-old if his body hadn't grown twice as fast as his head. He looked like a turtle and frightened the other children.

"Pray for Roberto's head," the neighbors said. "Pray that it will grow to fit his neck."

The neighbors in all the houses lit candles one Sunday and prayed to St. Gregory to give Roberto a bigger head. Even Mother lit candles as soon as Father drove away to his office. Except for Helen's family and ours, the whole neighborhood was Catholic, and that made Helen and me feel even closer. Roberto wasn't allowed to play outside after Mr. Garza's dogs chased him up our mimosa tree on Christmas Day. Roberto wore his new yellow knit hat with the bright orange pompom on top, a hat that all of us envied until Mr. Garza's pit bulls squeezed through the fence and chased Roberto up the pink flowering tree, the dogs jumping and nipping at the bobbing orange pompom, and Roberto trotting along as fast as his thick legs could run, and straight up the tree, hugging the bark for three hours before his mama could get him down.

I never saw Roberto after the week we lit candles and prayed to St. Gregory, but I heard that his head grew two sizes bigger in one night, and the next day his mama hung her best white handkerchief on the doorjamb and lit three extra candles in thanks to St. Gregory.

"Do you believe it?" Helen said.

"Of course. Miracles always happen to Catholics."

We told stories in the widow's orange tree until Mother's voice called me to dinner. One time I climbed too high on the new branches, and thorns sank into my flesh. I washed the dried streaks of blood off my legs with the hose, but Mother shook her head and slapped my thighs with a dishcloth.

"That animal," she muttered. "He is bad for your legs."

"Mother, you don't know Reuben. He's an angel."

"Is a goat," she sniffed, and stuffed my shirt and shorts into the washing machine.

"Father says superstition is from the Devil," I said.

"That *goat* is from the Devil. You do not talk to me about Father." I turned away, but she caught my elbow. "You not tell Father about the witch doctor." Her voice shook, like Paul's when he bounced on my knee, but hers was filled with fear. I looked in Mother's dark eyes, looked for some place to crawl into, some cradle to rock me. But they were so dark, I was lost.

"Please, not tell Father."

I touched her hand. "No. I won't tell."

Another Wednesday to the witch doctor. I reach up and pet Paul's head. His black hair curls around my fingers. He pushes my hand away and wraps his arms around Mother's neck. Mother smiles at me. I have her warm brown eyes for a moment, but I trip on a tar bump and grab her arm to keep from skinning my knees. "Watch where you go," Mother says and shakes her head. "You got chicken legs for your nine birthday?" Her eyes turn black, and she looks ahead.

We pass the dirty boy with the cap on the street again. For two years he has been roller-skating on the sidewalk. I hold my head high, but he skates in a circle and stares at me. I cover my breasts with my arms and walk, looking down at the moving concrete. Mother won't buy me a bra. She says I don't need a bra for raisins.

I noticed when my Mother and Father stopped looking at each other. Mother was weaving my hair into two long braids, and Father was reading a book on masonry in the chair across from me. If I stretched my foot out I could have touched my Father's knee, but I felt alone in the room with each of them.

Mother tugged at my hair, and her fingers moved swiftly around the three strands. Her jaw was straight and hard, and her hairline formed a straight black line on her forehead. Even her slender bones poked against her dress in hard edges. I strained to look at Mother through the corner of my eyes. My eye sockets hurt, but I liked looking at her brown lips. She twisted a band around the end of the braid and brushed the feathered tip against her cheek. She smiled at me, and all the edges disappeared in the soft curve of her cheek.

Father turned the page and took a sip of coffee from his mug. "Where's Paul?" his eyes still scanning the page.

And Mother, finished with my braid, looked at Father's black leather shoe. Maybe his wax shoestrings.

"Is sleeping for the nap," she said to his shoe.

He nodded and looked at the chair she sat in.

They spoke to each other's limbs and clothing, to the rug, the furniture. When I spoke, I found their eyes, but they couldn't find each other's.

III

Paul turned white and blue at recess and the teacher called Father. She threatened to call the police if Father took Paul to the church instead of a doctor. So Father took Paul to his doctor friend.

Mother was in the doctor's office with Paul, and Father and I sat in the waiting room. I opened a magazine and flipped the pages. I stopped at a survey, "Are You a Nymphomaniac?" and asked Father for a pencil. He took the magazine to the receptionist, shook his finger at her, then at me, then walked back to his seat and took a long breath.

"Rebecka, you are not to be alone with boys."

"I know, Father."

"You *haven't* been alone with a boy, have you?"

"No, Father."

"Good." He opened a home-decor magazine and turned a page. "That Helen doesn't talk about boys, does she?"

"No." Helen and I talked about *men*. We were going to marry men who were rich brothers and travel around the world. Helen already had a boyfriend at school, but the boy I liked, Lance Davis, was a year older, eleven, and his eyes were like Helen's blue crystal beads. He dropped his books once, and when I helped him gather them, I saw his bookmark with writing scrawled on it and tucked the bookmark in my pocket. In the bathroom, I pulled out the paper and smoothed it with my palm. *Reading Is Out of This World*, it said, above a green alien waving from his spaceship as he flew across a red planet. The other side said, *Michelle*, with a phone number underneath. The stolen bookmark burned like fire in my pocket for the rest of the school day.

That night at church, I left Paul by himself on the pew and went down and prayed to God at the sinner's bench. *Forgive me for stealing Lance's bookmark, Lord. Everyone knows he doesn't read anyway, and I've got more need for a bookmark than he does. Please let Michelle be his aunt, and please don't let me ever lose the bookmark, and please don't let me be the only girl in fifth grade without a boyfriend. Thank you and Amen.*

"I went through a lot of trouble to do this for you, Becka, so you'd better not say no." Helen and I were in the widow's orange tree, and Reuben was baaing at us to throw down the orange pulp. Helen pulled a large white sock with a soiled bottom out of her pocket. It reeked of sweat.

"This is going to save your love life," she said.

"A dirty sock?"

"It's a trick. Papa's sock and St. Anthony. A gift from the widow." She held up a small statue of a man in a robe, the one that sits with dozens of candles on the widow's table. She held the statue of St. Anthony between us.

"Tell St. Anthony who you love."

"Lance Davis," I told the statue.

"St. Anthony," Helen said, "make Lance fall in love with Rebecka. Amen." She put the statue upside down in the sock and hung it on a thorn in the orange tree. We climbed down and Helen explained.

"The widow told me St. Anthony has to stay upside down in there until he grants your wish. I thought of the dirty sock myself, to make him answer it faster. Lance will be in love with you for sure."

Michelle Williams was riding her bicycle to the park when a truck ran a red light and barreled over her. The truck dragged her seventy-five feet before the drunk driver stopped, but the local authorities said they were certain she died instantly. Helen and I gave St. Anthony back to the widow, and we didn't climb the orange tree for three weeks.

The table had been set up with the flowered tablecloth and tall white candles. Mother made *bandeja paiza* and *patacones* and used the best dishes in the house.

"I thought we were having fried chicken," Father said.

"In my country, Mama made *bandeja paiza* and *patacones* for the birthday. Now, I make for Paul."

"You didn't make it for my birthday," I said.

"You are not a boy," she said. I handed Father a cloth napkin and waited while he spread the cloth over his lap.

"Helen's birthday party is today," I said.

"You've told me that three times," he said. Mother carried in a cake that looked like whipped-up sea foam.

"It is your brother's birthday today," she said. "You want rather to party with friends and disgrace the family?"

I sat in the chair beside Father and watched him scoop the rice and meat mixture onto his plate. Mother sat beside Paul, wiped her forehead, and smiled. Paul poked his finger into the cake and made a hole, but Mother didn't slap his hand.

"You don't love your brother," she said.

"Yes I do." I looked at Paul, and I hated his skinny arms and small head. He stirred his rice and beans in little circles on his plate. Why don't you eat, I thought, eat, eat, eat. You're dying on purpose.

Father picked out pieces of pork and shoved them to the side of his plate. "You're getting too old to play with Helen. She's Jewish, you know."

"And I have work, now," Mother said. "You need to help watch your brother."

"Why? Do you have somewhere to go?" he asked. Mother and I looked at each other. Don't say the secret, I heard her through the black holes in her eyes. I won't, my eyes said back to her.

"No. No place to go. Just I need sometime to make walks to the store for milk." She twirled her fork on her plate. "Right, *Flaca*?"

"Right," I said, and looked at Father. "And I'm not lying."

"Of course you're not," Father said. "You're not a sinful child like some other children I see at church," he said. I watched him eat a bite and my stomach turned. I didn't feel sinful, except when I thought about the witch doctor's spider fingers too long, or when a lie was brewing in my stomach. I even gave Bethany my evil eye without feeling sinful. Sitting next to Father, I felt shamed, as I stared at Paul's foamy cake so Father wouldn't see my neck burning red.

Paul looked at me and smiled. The skin around his eye sockets were sunken with a tint of blue. His hair fell in long black curls around his face, and he looked so much like my mother.

"I just want to go to Helen's party," I said.

"Why don't you invite her to our church," said Father. "You don't want to play too much with people like her. God says the Jews are a stubborn people. Awful hard to convert, too."

Mother brushed a curl out of Paul's face and stroked his head. Her glazed eyes stared through Paul, out the kitchen window where the white long-haired seeds floated on the wind. A slow, rippling wheeze grew in Paul's chest.

"Mother," I said. "Can I go?"

"The air is not good today," she said.

The next Wednesday, I didn't want to sit in the kitchen with the professor, so I waited outside on the front porch and watched the children jump rope while Mother consulted with the witch doctor. It was the first sunny day in months, and the tenants crawled out of the brick houses and sat on the stoops and balconies, in old lounge chairs, sunning their faces. I still tasted the foam-mint icing on Paul's cake in the corner of my lips.

I thought about Helen's party. Some other girl was holding her hand and whispering secrets to her. The Other Girl and Helen were climbing up the widow's orange tree and the Other Girl was eating my oranges and spitting them down for Reuben. The Other Girl was a Jew or a Catholic, God's favorites, not like me, a nothing.

The dirty boy on skates rolled up to me and stopped. He was Mexican.

"Your mother at the witch lady?" he said.

"None of your business."

"You don't have to be mean. I know you. You been coming here a long time." He sat down on the porch step beside me. "You don't like it here? You're like us."

"No, I'm not. I'm *Colombian*."

The sun reflected a brilliant heat off his black hair. He didn't look so dirty up close, and he only shrugged his shoulders at my insult. He crossed his leg and spun the skate wheels with his fingers, and I realized he wasn't going away. I talked.

"My mother thinks the witch doctor can cure my brother. He's got asthma. She's crazy."

The boy nodded. "That's okay. My father's crazy, too. Really *loco*. I don't know where he is now, but he used to live in Mexico with Mama. When he passed people on the street, they nodded, their hats real low. But richer people and strangers called him *loco*," and when the boy spoke the word, he twisted up his mouth and squinted his eyes in pure meanness, and said again in a low voice, "*Loco*."

"Why?" I said. The heat from his hair made my skin ripple with warm bumps.

"One day he rode through town on his horse, only he didn't have no clothes on. The people were mad and told my older brothers to make him get down and cover himself. So my brothers—I have four— followed my father and asked him to come down. He said, 'I can't!' And they said, 'Why?' And you know why he couldn't come down?"

I shook my head.

"He said, 'Because the sun told me to.' He said the rays from the sun wouldn't let him get down. He rode all the day on the horse until the priest found out and came to the house. The priest said, 'Who is making you do this?' and my father said, 'The sun's rays.' Then the priest took out an old sword—like from the Mexican war or something—and swung it all around the air until he was sweating. Then he said to my father, 'Now I have broken the rays and you are free to get down.' My father said, 'Thank you,' and he climbed down and went in the house. That's crazy."

He said his name was Tomaso. He opened his palm and put it on my lap. "Can you do fortunes?"

I picked up his hand with my thumb and forefinger and put it back on his knee. "I killed a girl at school last month. With a prayer and a dirty sock. I don't trust myself."

Mother carried Paul down the witch doctor's porch steps and kicked my leg softly. "Get up, *Flaca*. Your father will be home soon."

Tomaso said goodbye, but I ran after Mother, whose black figure scuttled up the street against a brightening orange sunset. When I turned around to wave at Tomaso, he was gone.

In the middle of the night, Father turned on the light and threw my sheets up off my legs.

"Up," he said. His voice was soft and strange. I sat up and rubbed my eyes, and he wrapped the sheet hastily around my shoulders.

"Where are we going?" I said.

"To Helen's."

My heart leaped in my throat and I reached around his waist and squeezed. "Thank you, Father. Thank you, thank you."

Mother walked past my door with Paul bundled in a blanket, his limp hand hanging over her shoulder. She stopped and turned to us. Her bundled hair fell in sad strings around her neck, and she stroked Paul's back delicately, as though he were a newborn kitten. I let go of Father and covered my mouth in shame.

"Let's go to your Helen's," she said softly.

IV

I knew my brother was going to die. Twenty doctors couldn't have helped him. He was drowning in the air, the same blue air I sucked in and spit out. I was too young to understand. Did I steal his air? After the funeral, I held my breath under my grass-green blanket and tried to hold back all the air I breathed that had belonged to him. The funeral. In front of my brother's white body.

Father had whiskers under his chin, a tuft of hair he missed while shaving, surrounded by skin smooth as a leather Bible. Mother's face gleamed with tears that slid into our palms and made my hand itch and her hand too slippery to hold. The harder I squeezed, the more my hand slipped from hers. That night, I dreamed Paul was a baby again, swimming in heaven, and heaven was a giant aquarium, and God's mansion was ice crystal and the air was liquid blue, the kind of blue that gold and white shimmering fish swim in at Japanese restaurants. Paul lumbered through the water like a turtle, his tiny arms and legs stretching and wading, and the witch doctor blew a curl of smoke into his face and laughed and said, "*Tienes que hacerte una limpia.*" And baby Paul laughed and traced monkeys in the liquid smoke. He squealed, "*Flaca, Flaca, Flaca!*" but his words were swallowed by hovering bubbles and popped. It was heaven, but I did not want to be there.

I was relieved when I woke up in my own sweat and breathed deeply, greedily, the night air.

Tuesday, and Mother wraps her fist in a white dishcloth. I sit deep in the corner of the couch, knees tucked under my chin, and I watch Mother's hand sweep in rhythm across the doorframe. The room is dark. Vases of white roses, wreaths of carnations, lilies of the valley, and unopened cards decorate the tables and floors, but the smell of jasmine overpowers them. The jasmine plant sent by someone named Ellingson, with condolences. I stretch my foot out and touch the white petals, and a small blossom falls to the carpet.

Mother draws back the living-room curtain and sunlight falls across my legs. The small hairs on my knees glisten and rise under the goose pimples. I hear the tree next door moaning from the weight of the tire swing. Reuben's soft *baa*s float across the street. Mother frowns, and in my mind, I see the goat leaning all his weight against his tether, reaching for an orange peel Helen has thrown from the widow's tree. Everything is quiet, but the air is kindling.

Mother sprays the window and wipes it in circles. She turns and looks at me for the first time since the funeral yesterday. Yes, I think. Tell me. Talk to me, Mother. I untuck my legs and put my feet on the floor, so she doesn't waste her words on manners. Her dark eyes are wet pools, brimming at the edges. She opens her mouth, but God interrupts us. A bird slams against the window with a deafening thump. Mother and I jump and we stare at the bird who has already tumbled to the front porch. We both lean over and stare at the limp bird, large and black, a no-good crow that everybody hates, but no one wants to see die. It's bad luck to see a black bird die. His sleek body is still and purple and perfect for a moment, and he is never more beautiful than now. Almost instantly, he shakes his feathers, hops up, and stumbles across the cement like a drunken sailor.

I breathe a sigh.

"Is a bad sign," Mother says. "Crows, they carry death. More death."

No, I think, no. The witch doctor is crazy. Birds are birds, and Paul is *not* a bird or a cigar or a wrinkle in your palm. But I can't say anything to Mother because when I look up, Father is standing behind her.

Father's shoulders slump, and he looks like a very old man in need of a cane. He breathes a loud sigh and shakes his head. "Bad signs," he says.

Mother turns to Father, but doesn't look at him. Her head tilted down, the back of her neck long and limp, she reminds me of the broken bird.

Then Mother falls to her knees, and she is like a stone figure, staring past the carpet to a deeper world. Father puts his hand on her head and pats it softly.

"Paul is in heaven," he says. "God is holding his hand right now, and they're both looking down at us and wondering why we're so sad. Paul can finally breathe. He's happy now." But he says it as though he's trying to convince himself.

Mother's shoulders tremble, and at first, small whimpers rise from her throat. But they grow louder and stronger until her wails shake the air around me. I watch her in her misery, wanting to cry, wanting to fall on her back and cry for Paul, too, but my eyes are wide and dry. Her head sinks lower and lower until it rests on the carpet, her arms splayed out in front of her. I have never seen her this way. Father nods to me, and I slowly walk to my bedroom.

"Paul," she screams as I lie on my bed, my hands over my ears. "My baby. Paul." I can still hear her, and Father's shushing whispers on her hair.

Can Paul hear Mother screaming for him? I wish she would scream my name. Rebecka. My Rebecka. But she cries for Paul, and I listen and wait for them to open my door and say, Come to us, now, our beautiful girl. They forget me, until it is dinner, and they realize I'm not outside. When they open my bedroom door, they think my cheeks are puffed and wet for my brother's death.

I understood why I wasn't allowed to play outside the first few days after the funeral. But a week passed, then two, and I was still locked in the house. Mother didn't cry anymore, but moved her arms mechanically in circles, in arches, as though if she stopped moving, a sadness would cave in around her. I found her in the kitchen, moving her hands in circles. She cooked casseroles and empanadas, breads, cakes, flan, and the refrigerator slowly filled each day with unbroken breads and sealed dishes. Her skin glistened in the August heat of the kitchen, and I felt as though I were stepping into the mouth of hell when I pushed open the kitchen door.

"Mother, I haven't seen Helen for sixteen days. It's like a prison in here."

Mother stirred meat in a saucepan, and thick steam floated into the vent. "You can play in the yard. In back."

"The backyard?" I ground my teeth together and grunted. "Why?"

"The yard is nothing wrong. Is nice place to play."

"Mother, I'm not a goat."

"No, you are a girl. My girl," she said. "And you will not be hurt. There is too many bad spirits in the streets."

"I'm almost eleven years old. I can take care of myself."

"Possible. Hand me the onion." I picked up a red onion, beaded with water, and placed it in her hand, but I didn't let go.

"Mother," I said, "summer's almost over. I'll die in here."

Her eyes widened and before I blinked, I felt the warm sting of her hand slapping my cheek. "How you dare," she said. "How you dare." She had never slapped me before.

"Mother," I said, holding my cheek with one hand and guarding my face with the other. The onion fell to the floor and bumped across the linoleum.

Mother shook her head, then grabbed my shoulders and pulled me to her breast. I felt her trembling, smelled her warm skin, felt her heart in my ears. I was ashamed of myself, feeling such happiness in her arms. I cried and pressed my burning cheek into her breast.

From my bedroom, I saw Helen skipping rope on the sidewalk. Maria stood beside her with a jump rope under her arm, and hanging from her left wrist, the green purse I gave Helen the summer before. I pressed my nose against the windowpane and watched Maria dig her hands in the green purse and pull out a tube of lipgloss. Helen sang, "Cinderello, dressed in yellow, went upstairs to kiss her fellow. Made a mistake and kissed a snake—"

I squinted my eyes and stared a hole into Maria's mouth, and prayed my evil eye would make Maria's lips fall off. Helen was *my* friend. She belonged to me.

Wednesday, and Mother lies in bed with a wet rag on her forehead. Her eyes are bloated and her cheeks have red patches. Father pulls me from the room and we drive together to church. Our church used to have a big white neon cross. The building sits in a broad low ditch beside the highway, and only its roof peeks out over the road. The elders voted on raising a fourteen-foot cross on a pole so potential visitors would know we had a church down there, and everyone thought it was a good idea. But when the pastor's brother pulled into the church lot with a white neon cross tied to the back of his pickup, the elders started whispering.

Then the pastor's brother flipped a switch, and neon red cursive letters flowed across the white T, spelling "Jesus Saves," and the elders started grumbling. But it was too late. The cross was paid for and delivered, and the only thing to do was put it up. I liked it. The cross glowed a white halo at night, and sometimes it blinked at me when we drove home—Jesus Saves. Jesus Saves. Jesus Saves. A few years later, when the pastor was voted out of the church, he dug up the cement block and strapped his neon cross on top of his moving van and carried it away, leaving us a big hole in front of the church.

"Mother will feel better tomorrow," Father says. The night unfolds early, and the August heat seeps through the vents. Father doesn't like the silence of the road.

"You think so?"

"We'll pray for her tonight." His eyes are on the road. Mine are on the stars, twinkling in the black pool of the night. The floating stars remind me of Mother's eyes. And then I am angry. Mother at home buried alive in bed, trying to bury me alive with her, and me having to go with Father to church to pray for her. I will pray for Paul, and I will pray for Helen, and I will even pray for Tomaso and Maria who stole my green purse, and I will pray for my eleventh birthday party, but I will not pray for Mother tonight.

I fell asleep in church and dreamed I was bouncing Paul on my knees. His black hair flew in long curls and grew longer and longer until he had Mother's hair and Mother's eyes, and suddenly he was Mother and I was bouncing on her knees. She leaned over and kissed me on the forehead. I awoke in the sanctuary as Father, gentle and quiet, scooped me up and carried me to the car. He cradled me into his chest, and a faint trace of cream and spice swirled in my head. My legs and arms felt weightless, and although my feet kept bumping his knees, I felt small and soft, like a caterpillar. When I was six he told me I was too big to be carried, but I saw it wasn't so.

V

I didn't mean to do it, but I was impatient, and I missed Helen, and the house closed off from air was beginning to breed a thick aroma of Paul.

If I had known.

Mother whisked eggs in a glass bowl, the whisk and her fingers a blur of circles, and I sat at the table, watching a loaf of bread tucked under a thin cloth. I peeked under the cloth at the doughy mound. It was white and soft like Paul's skin at the funeral, skin so transparent and smooth I wanted to touch it. I poked a small hole in the bottom of the dough with my finger, but it didn't whoosh and deflate like it would in a cartoon. Mother poured olive oil on the saucepan.

"I want to go to Helen's," I said.

"Maybe tomorrow." Mother turned and smiled at me, but her eyebrows rose up anxiously.

"Why not today?"

"Well, you never know. After Paul, bad things—"

"I'm sick of bad things," I said. My throat felt too small for my voice, and something heavy and tight shook my body, like a train roaring up my spine.

If only I had known he needed to wipe his tears.

"I'm sick of bad luck," I yelled, "and I'm sick of this house. I'm sick of your cleaning rags—he's not here anymore, Mother. Paul's dead. He's dead! But I'm *not*—I'm still here. It doesn't matter if you go back to the witch doctor—she can't bring him back!"

Mother's hands dropped into the egg yolk. I heard a puff of air, and I knew that Father was behind me.

"I'm not going to the witch doctor's anymore," I said again. My heart beat against my ears.

"You've been going to a witch doctor?" Father squeezed the tissue in his hand and his voice was low and cold. I nodded my head, but I kept thinking Helen, Helen, Helen, I'm coming. I stood between Father and Mother, but he looked right through me, to the back of Mother's black head, and then I knew he wasn't speaking to me. I wasn't even there.

"You've been going to a witch doctor?" he said louder. Mother stared into the pool of yolk.

"Answer me!" he yelled. His voice exploded in the heat of the kitchen, and I flinched at the intensity.

"Yes," Mother whispered.

"When?"

She didn't speak, and he pushed me aside and stepped toward her.

"When?" he said again. He grabbed her arm and jerked her around. Her jaw was clenched, but her eyes sparked as she stared into his face.

"On Wednesdays," she said.

"Wednesdays? You said you were sick—and I was at church praying for my son—and you were undoing all my prayers by going straight to the Devil?"

His hands shook, and I waited for him to hit Mother. I was afraid he might crush her head with his hands. But his words crushed her instead.

"You killed him," he shouted. "You killed our son by turning your back against God." I thought Mother would sink into the floor or cry out or faint, but her face was a stone mask, and it was Father whose voice broke into sobs. "You killed my baby son. When I was praying every day for him, every second. You lost him. Paul!" He dropped to the floor, as though she had broken his legs, and his heavy sobs burned my eardrums. "Look what you've done," he cried.

He reached for the chair leg and thrust the chair backward. It crashed to the floor, and then I screamed. I covered my ears, turned around, and ran away from Father on his knees and my stone mother. Out the front door into the hot dusk, the entire street bathed in golden haze, and my head crashing with cymbals and my feet slapping the pavement, taking me away from the death house where I was suffocating, where the air was too thick to breathe.

I ran without thinking, without seeing. My hands opened a wooden gate and my feet climbed the trunk of a tree. The sharp smell of rind filled my nose and my eyes opened again. I was in the widow's orange tree. I held my breath to slow the panting in my breast. The tree had changed since Paul's funeral. The white blossoms had disappeared, and in their place small green orbs stuck out like rubber lollipops. I squeezed one, but it was hard and broke from the stem into my hand.

"What are you doing up there?" The widow's voice startled me. She tapped on the tree with her cane. "You're going to knock down all my oranges. Get down here."

"I don't want to come down," I said. My nose was running, and I wiped it with my hand.

"It's getting dark, child."

"I don't care."

"Aren't you afraid of the bats?"

"You don't have bats."

"I might tonight. Bats are unpredictable."

The widow stretched her neck to get a better look at me. She inched around the trunk of the tree.

"I'm not coming down," I said.

"Ever? Don't you want to eat?"

"I'll eat the oranges when they get ripe."

"The mosquitoes will eat you first," she said.

My head hurt and my eyes stung. I thought of Father on the kitchen floor, of Mother's forehead on the carpet, of Paul's white casket on the mound of dirt. The earth was swallowing up my family. I would stay up in the branches.

"I guess that means I'm coming up," the widow said. Then I heard a scuffling on the bark, and the sound of feet slipping, and a grunt, and a limb creak. The old woman grabbed and huffed and clutched and pulled, and only when I saw her white head rise like a soft cloud through the leaves did I believe her. Her arms quivered as she scooted her large bottom onto the cross branch beside mine. Her flower-print dress was smudged brown and her bony ankles hung from beneath a ripped hem. The limbs entwined beneath us were large, sturdy, comfortable. The old woman straightened her glasses, which had slipped down on her nose. She heaved a sigh, and pulled a green bulb from the branch. She smelled it.

"Looks like we'll be up here a good while if you're determined to eat my oranges."

I stared into Helen's yard. Reuben chewed on a mound of hay. The sunset cast a golden glow on the yard. I knew the widow had been cutting rosemary because she brought the scent of it into the tree. The blend of orange and rosemary slowed the churning in my brain.

"What's wrong, child?"

She was the first person since the funeral to ask me, and I didn't want to talk, but the words forced their way out. "Me. I'm wrong. I'm a mistake. Father thinks it's Mother's fault. But it's mine." She touched my cheek, and before I could worry about falling, my head was on her shoulder, and my tears rolled onto her cotton dress.

"I was mean to my brother. It's my fault he died."

"No, it's not." The widow stroked my hair.

Then I cried hard, and my body shook the leaves.

"Yes it is. You don't know what I thought. Mother loved him more than me, and I wished he would disappear, and now he's dead, and it's my fault because I wished it in the first place. Just like I killed Michelle—"

"Now you hush that," the widow said. "What kind of strange ideas are crawling into your ears? Killing Michelle. A drunk driver killed that poor girl, not you. And what do you mean your mother loved Paul more than you? She loves you enough to keep you indoors, away from anything that might hurt you, as crazy as that might seem to you or me."

The widow lifted my head off her lap and held my chin in her hand. She pulled the stray wet hairs out of my face and tucked them behind my ears. She looked solid and sturdy balanced there in the orange tree, not like the frail old widow from the earth below.

"And we all wish our brothers and sisters would disappear for a day or two so we can have our mothers all to ourselves. But wishes are just that, and nothing else. They're not swords or knives. They're not asthma, child."

"My father hates my mother."

"He found out, did he? Well, the whole neighborhood was waiting for that. But don't worry yourself too long. It's natural. People are always looking for answers in different places, and when they find out there are no answers, it's terribly hard."

The lightning bugs began glowing beneath our feet.

"This is a very comfortable salon you have," she said, "but I have to be going inside. I have a guest coming for brownies and soda. I would invite you to join Helen and me, but I understand you need to stay up here and wait for my oranges to get ripe—"

I was on the ground before the widow finished her sentence, and cupped my hands for her feet as she climbed down. Inside the house, we lit candles, stirred flour and chocolate with a wooden spoon, and waited for Helen.

I remember before Paul was born. Mother lit eight white candles, one for every month she carried Paul in her womb. I remember the kitchen was dark, like a secret. She stood over the candlelight, her face lit up like the moon, her round belly a peony in full bloom, and she prayed to St. Gregory. "Please come, señor, please the baby." Then in Spanish, unfamiliar words that danced in my ears. I passed my hand over the candle as I'd seen Father do and watched the flame bounce and the smoke twist up in black curls. Eight white candles on a clean white cloth. Clean because St. Gregory is the saint of surgery and he likes things sanitized.

"Not touch the table," she whispered to me hoarsely, and moved my hands away from the white tablecloth. "Pray for the baby." She held my hands like a flower bud in her cupped hands. Her dark liquid eyes poured straight into mine and down to my stomach. Then she placed my hands on her belly, and the baby's elbow rolled under my palm. Mother laughed like a song.

The widow snuffed out the candles one by one around the statue of St. Anthony. The brass bell sucked up the flame, and the widow sang.

Tengo a San Antonio puesto de cabeza,
Si no me vusca un novio ya nadie lo endereza.

Helen and I held hands under the table. Her curly locks were tied back in ladybug barrettes, and her almond eyes flashed at me. She locked her ankle under mine and we swung our legs back and forth. The warm chocolate stuck to our teeth and hardened under the cold soda. We laughed at the widow's terrible singing.

"It's a silly song my mama used to sing to me when I was twenty and didn't have a beau," she said. "You shouldn't ever blow out candles. It uses up energy, and it disturbs the oxygen in the room. Always use a candlesnuffer."

She told us the story about how she met her husband, Elias, in the big city. How she had bought a large spool of thread at the dime store and placed it in her straw basket. The spool fell out when she packed her sourdough loaf, but the end of the thread was snagged on the basket. When Elias stepped on the spool, with not two inches of blue thread wrapped around it, and picked it up, and when he saw the thread trailing out the door of the bakery, it seemed only natural to him to start winding. So he did. He wound the thread out the door, down the sidewalk, into the card shop, around the crystal glass display, out the card shop, and across the street to a little cafe where the widow, who was young and beautiful, sat drinking her coffee with two lumps of sugar. He held out the lumpy, frayed spool.

"The thread was useless," the widow said laughing. "But I offered him a cup of coffee, and he offered me his bakery store, which really was his heart. Of course, I had been working my charms on him for months. I bought bread, cakes, cookies, bagels, donuts—he must have thought I owned stock in flour—but he never once looked into my eyes. But the thread—the *thread*—knew what to do."

Before I walked home, Helen placed a small bell in my hand and closed my fingers over it.

"It's from Reuben's collar," she said. "Ring it when you miss me."

6

For days, Mother lay still under her blanket, and did not lay out my clothes or clean them or cook dinner or wash the dishes. Mornings when I padded into the kitchen, Father, always awake and dressed, sipped his coffee in a trance. The newspaper lay on the table untouched. Each morning a bizarre routine. I poured milk into my cereal and broke Father's silent trance with my crunching. He opened the morning paper and shook the pages. Then, finding nothing of interest, he grunted and let the papers fall to the floor, stood up, patted his pockets for the jingle of keys, then walked out the door. Our house was a tomb.

One week before the new school year began, Father jingled his keys, opened the door and stopped. He walked toward me and leaned down. I felt five again, with mashed cake under my lip, and I closed my eyes and waited for Father to kiss me. For a moment, the world was quiet and black and I was afraid he had walked out the door. Then he did it. I felt his lips like feathers on my forehead, which too quickly disappeared. He patted my head, and I heard his footsteps and the creak of the door. Then I opened my eyes and wondered if I had dreamed the kiss.

Mother stopped eating, so I made her toast and heated a bowl of

Lori Ann Stephens

chicken soup. As I opened her door, the odor of sweaty sheets and dead roses filled my nose. She kept the room dark, and when my eyes adjusted, I carried the tray to her bedside. She didn't move. I watched the blanket for the slow rise of her breathing, and when the blanket didn't move either, I panicked and sat down on the bed beside her and pulled the coverlet off her head. She groaned and rolled over.

"I brought you some food," I whispered.

"*Gracias,*" she said, but she had turned over with a finality that I knew meant *Leave me alone.*

Father left for work and came home late. Mother stayed in bed. It didn't take long for me to realize I could sneak outside and play again. The girls on the street played hopscotch on limestone squares. Helen and I climbed the widow's orange tree. I tiptoed into the Stein's back-yard and stroked Reuben's wiry coat, and Helen made Maria give back the green purse. The last sighs of summer drenched my body with life, and I twirled and skipped all day, intoxicated by the elixir of the dripping sun. But I had to climb the steps to my house at the end of each day, and every night, Mother still slept in her bed, her room filling with the stink of death.

One Wednesday as I walked down the hall, I saw her standing in her bedroom. In shock, I stopped and stared at her body, rail-thin beneath the sheer nightgown, an apparition. She scared me for a moment—I wondered if it was my mother or the ghost of my mother—but I realized that I was too old to be afraid of ghosts. It was then that I realized that I'd missed my eleventh birthday the day before. Everyone had forgotten, even me. Then Mother slowly padded to bed, brushing her hand against the closing door.

It was Helen's idea to go back to the witch doctor. Helen and I sat in the bus, not too far back where strange men with beards might get ideas, and not too close to the front, where the bus driver might think we were running away from home. I patted the scissors in my vest pocket. I had ridden the route to the witch doctor's street many times, I had told Helen the day before, but the streets and the buildings and

Glimmer Train Stories

even the belching and squealing of the bus were strange to me as we held hands and watched the outside world blur past us.

We had been catching doodle-bug wives for Helen's bug farm. "Absolutely not," I said. We hunted along the grass edges of the pavement. "I don't ever want to go there again."

"But what if she can help your mom?" Helen said. "What if you take back everything the witch doctor gave you?"

"She didn't give us anything. And I don't believe her, anyway."

"But your mom does."

"That doesn't make it real," I said.

"It's real for her."

I thought about Mother all night. I dreamed we were walking down the long street to the witch doctor, and each step we took, the farther away the witch doctor's brown house stretched from us. Old men, ragged women carrying babies on their hips, and dirty children stood on their stoops and called out to me, "But your mother believes her, Rebecka. She believes." I woke in the damp coolness of my pillow, my neck wet from sweat. As my room shifted from black to blue morning, dreams flashed in my sleep.

Mother, dressed in a white breezy dress and a straw hat, pushed me on a tire swing. I smiled, and the air was cool through my teeth, and the breeze lifted the small hairs on my legs. I heard Mother's laughter like distant bells. "You want to go higher?" she said behind me.

"Yes," I said. "Higher."

As I rose up over her head, I felt her hands on my bottom, and I looked down at her smiling face, which reminded me of a butterfly. Then she pushed, and down and out my body twirled on the tire, and I rose up higher than the tallest branch on the tree.

"Say hello to Paul for me," Mother cried below me. "Say we love him."

I looked up in the sky. "Hello, Paul. Paul?" But all I saw were clouds and a hummingbird that didn't belong so high in the sky.

When I awoke the next day, I waited for Father to close the front door, then I dressed, peeked at Mother through the crack of her door, and sneaked out of the house to Helen's with two bus passes in my pocket.

"Did you bring the scissors?" Helen asked.

I pulled them out of my pocket. The bus bounced and we grabbed each other's arm for support. Mother had paid the witch doctor with her grocery allowance, but we had no money to pay the witch doctor. We read that witches used toads and lizards in potions, and although we couldn't find any creatures on the way to the bus stop, we did have our hair. I handed Helen the scissors, and turned my back to her, and she pulled my hair straight with her hand.

"What if she won't take it?" I said.

"She will. Witches always need hair. Our hair is like the widow's thread. It will know what to do."

My hair was not very long, but it passed my shoulders enough that I could chew on a rope of it when I went to the movies. I heard the snip-snip of the scissors, then Helen's hand thrust a bundle of cinnamon-colored hair in front of me. I reached behind my head and felt the tips of my hair. It ended in a soft jagged line against my neck.

"Now it's my turn," she said, and handed me the scissors.

I squeezed her dark curls in my hand and raked my fingers down and pulled the hair straight.

"You won't get in trouble?" I asked.

"It's okay."

"You don't have to do this."

"My hair is longer and prettier than yours. We'd better take some, just in case." She was right, so I pulled it down and only cut a piece the length of my hand on the right side. I left the left side long and curly, in case she missed her long hair.

The bus turned onto Greenlawn Avenue, which had no green and no lawns, but an endless stretch of two-story brownstones bordered by cracked pavement and black iron guardrails.

We knocked on the door for five minutes. No one answered. It didn't occur to me that the witch doctor might not be home. She was always home when Mother and I visited. Helen and I turned around and sat on the top stair.

Looking out across the street, I watched the cars drive the long road toward us and turn abruptly as the street curved left in front of the witch doctor's house. We looked for a man with soda-bottle-thick glasses and a dark woman in a broom skirt in each car as it drove past, in the crowd of people waiting at the bus stop and in the few that descended from the bus, and on the sidewalk, where the children swung on the lampposts and played on the fire escapes, trying to squeeze out every last ounce of summer. No sign of the witch doctor. The hair was hot in my hand, and when I opened my palm, the bundle of cinnamon and chocolate-colored hair was wet and tangled and stuck to my skin.

We walked down the stairwell and sat down again on the lowest step. Helen patted my back to comfort me. Tomaso rolled up to us on wheels, his hair combed and shiny and slicked back like a wet cat.

"You come here for the witch doctor?" he said.

"Yeah," I said.

"She's not here."

I felt as though my eyes would burst, but I gritted my teeth and clenched the wad of hair. Helen's pats came faster, as though the rhythm would somehow counteract the bad news.

"We have an emergency. A problem," Helen said.

"Too bad," he said. Then he sat down beside me and flipped up his skate and rolled the wheels with his palm. "My grandma says that when people in Ecuador—that's where she's from—when they have a big problem, they used to climb up to the volcano and pray to God, and she took spoons and forks for some reason—I don't know why. But we don't have no volcano here."

"It might help if we climbed something high," said Helen.

"What's that in your hand?" he said.

I showed him the bundle of hair.

"Is that yours? Can I have some?"

I gave him the whole wad of hair. Helen looked at Tomaso's brown legs. They were barely touching mine, but they felt like electricity on my skin.

"I got a story for you. It's for grown-ups," he said low. We leaned in to hear.

"My brother says that this island in the Galapagos used to be a prison, and they would send all the bad men there away from Ecuador. Some of the men had to stay there a long, long time. They got lonely for women, so they snuck out to the beach and did it with the seals, 'cause they're shaped like women down there."

"That's gross," Helen said. I wondered if it was true.

"I guess you won't be coming back no more," he said.

"No. I guess not," I said.

We stood up and he followed us to the bus stop. The sun cast its white heat on our heads, and we squinted in the bright sunlight. He rolled in circles around us until the bus squealed to a stop in a pool of black smoke. As I walked up the steps, he called to me, "Hey girl, I think you're pretty. *Muy linda.*" I smiled, and Helen rolled her eyes. I waved at him and followed Helen to the middle of the bus.

As I sat, I remembered the bookmark in my back pocket. Lance Davis. I pulled the bent bookmark out and traced the alien waving at me. I flipped it over. Michelle's name had worn away, rubbed off by the hot summer months it spent in my jeans, damp from sweat. I hopped up and ran to the door.

"Wait," I shouted to the driver. I stepped down and held the bookmark out to Tomaso through the open door. He took it, smiled at me, and made antennas with his fingers against his head. "My name is Rebecka," I said as the doors unfolded and closed. I watched him roll away, putting the bookmark in his back pocket.

"Lance is cuter," Helen said as the bus pulled away.

"Yeah," I said. "Much cuter." But *muy linda* sang in my head the entire ride home.

I crept back into the house, but there was no need to be careful. Mother still slept. The house was dark like a cocoon, like a womb. I walked to Mother's room and opened her door. It was after noon, and although I felt a twisting fist in my stomach, I wasn't hungry. Her body was still, but I heard soft, swollen whistles as she breathed through her nose. I closed the door quietly and crawled into my own bed.

The linens had not been changed for three weeks. My pillow smelled warm and dank, like morning sweat. The tiny, hard balls of cotton stuck to the sheets like ant eggs and made my legs itch. It was dark and silent when I pulled the grass-green blanket over my head, and I curled up into a ball, like Mother.

Under the sheets, my pocket of air warmed and burned my nostrils. This is Mother's air, I thought. I breathed deeply, sucked in the thin air until my brain warmed and tingled. The air began to hum in my ears, and I heard the slosh of distant beating, my heart knocking against my eardrum. The sounds broke the silence of the house. I listened to the soft beats, distant like a drum under water, like the feet of soldiers marching on a field of snow. Like a bass violin plunking through burlap. I heard music. I pushed off the blanket and sat up, releasing my breath, listening for the sounds. But just as quickly, it was silent again, a terrifying silence more suffocating than my cotton womb.

I crawled out of bed and walked to the kitchen. The sun-baked counters, half-filled bowls of hardened cereal, crumpled napkins, knives, and prescription bottles stared at me. The living room, too, was cluttered, Father's blankets on the couch and hundreds of dead flowers in vases of molded water. Everything still and warm, asphyxiated.

The organ sat lonely in the corner. I opened the shoebox on top of the organ, shook the cassettes inside, and picked a yellow one labeled "Let the Earth Praise God." I slid it into the deck and watched the black tape unravel in slow, squeaking circles. I knelt below the keyboard and sat on the rug. My legs stretched out against the speaker, the wooden pedals that once propped up my ankles were under my knees. I leaned my head against the brown burlap and listened.

"God?" I whispered. "I'm here again."

God had talked to me once before when I was quiet, and now that the entire house had stopped breathing, I knew that there was more silence here than an entire kingdom of mice. I whispered to the burlap speaker as though it were the ear of God.

"I know you took Paul away. Why couldn't you just give him more air here? I had plenty to share." But I knew I wouldn't have even shared a paper clip with Paul if he had asked me, and it made my head throb. "But why?" I said. I listened and waited, pressed my ear against the fabric, but God didn't answer. He was as absent as Paul was. He took my brother to a blue world where everything is still. I crawled out from under the organ and looked at the cassette deck. The tape had broken, and the plastic teeth on the wheel turned like open, mute mouths.

I turned to the kitchen and started putting away the clean dishes, washing the bowls and knives, opening cabinets, hoping to find my mother somewhere in the routine, looking for her in my own move-ments so I could pull her out of me and make her my mother again. I needed her to say, "Yes, we are alone now. And you are worth clean-ing a spoon, putting my feet on the cold floor, worth opening my eyes in the morning and living the rest of today." I tied her green scarf around my head. "You are my *Flaca*, my little white mouse." I wrapped my hand in a white dishcloth. "You have my eyes and my ears," I heard her say as I wiped the china cabinet in small circles like halos.

I sang softly, "The little girl cried, 'Oh the moon is a moon, and not a mother or father.'" And I stopped to listen for Mother this time instead of God. "And she slept in a crater that swallowed her up, but her tears left a body of water." I wiped the glass doors, but the streaks of dirt kept moving, and my cotton fist was turning black from the dust that had collected since Paul's death. I don't want to be swal-lowed up, I thought.

I was suddenly afraid that Mother lay too still in bed. Afraid of the heavy bedclothes, afraid of my own bound black fist, afraid that there was too much dust to clean, that soon we would be buried in Paul's dust. And then I heard the noise again, the slow steady rhythm, that made me stand up and told me to go to her.

I stare at the lumpy blanket that has swallowed my Mother whole, and the fist turns and opens in my stomach. I hear a rushing in my ears and the train returns to my spine and rushes up my neck.

"Mother," I say. My hands tremble. "Mother?"

I walk to the window and push back the curtains. Light floods the room, and I am no longer afraid of the dark. But the roaring in my head doesn't stop. I cross to her and poke her with my finger.

"Mother?"

She moans softly under the cover. "Mother?" I say again. Then I cry. All the loneliness, all the hushed evenings, the absence of her hands, the silence of her eyes, all the days spent curled in her own bed rise in my throat.

"Mother!" I shout. I grab the sheets and throw them off her body. Mother's head is tucked like a frightened squirrel, stiff and surprised, in her thin gown. "Mother, get out of bed. Get out of bed this instant!" I cry. "You *have* to take care of me. You're selfish lying there in bed. You only care about yourself. But I'm still here, Mother. I'm your child, and I'm still alive, and you don't even know I'm here!" The tears pour out of my eyes and I cannot stop them.

"Please, Mother. I'm your baby, too. Please. I'm still here. Look at me and tell me I'm still here."

She lifts her head off the pillow and opens her black eyes to me, and I jump. Right into her eyes, my soul jumps, and I swim in the dark cool depths. "Rebecka," her voice shakes. She touches my hair and twirls it in her fingers. "Your hair, *Flaca*." And I see my reflection, wading there in my mother's eyes. She reaches her hands to me, and I fall into her arms, and she rocks me with her whole body. I feel the warm tingling comfort in my legs, the caress of love in my veins, and I choke on my tears. We cry for us, for Paul, for the pain of death, and the pain of living birth.

The Last Pages

*Elise Catharine Henriette Buhmann Burmeister,
born mid-1800s to Joachim Hinrich Buhmann
and Maria Dorothea Elisabeth Selig Buhmann.*

My new book of short stories, *Had a Good Time*, which will be published in August this year, is built around my extensive collection of picture postcards from the first two decades of the twentieth century. I've collected these cards not so much for the pictures on the front (although the images are often quite interesting, too) but for the messages written on the backs. Before telephones were common, people would sometimes pour their hearts out on the postcards they wrote. I have a wonderful collection of these very brief but highly intense and suggestive messages from people long-since dead. So I chose my fifteen favorite ones and either picked up the voices off the cards or the voices of people referred to in the cards and I wrote the fully-imagined, first-person stories. As soon as I read this reference to Hiram in an antique shop in North Carolina, he began talking to me.

—*Robert Olen Butler*

My mother and father have always struck me as a strange and beautiful pair. This was a common source of confusion to me as a child, to see them as such and then to meet a world that found them strange for reasons so different than my own, to meet a world that did not find them beautiful.

—*Jennifer Tseng*

I am incapable of buying real estate. Everyone tells me that my payments to a landlord make no sense, that now, especially, well into mid-adulthood, I should care about equity. The truth is, I *do* care about equity, just not that kind. And from where I write the monthly checks that accrue nothing in return, I have a harbor view I could never afford to "own." Nevertheless, for years I've been going to Sunday open houses, looking at modest bungalows and condos. I have felt defeated and incompetent after some of these fruitless hunts, free and unburdened or triumphantly savvy after others, and always bewildered by what owners have *done* with those places. Long past the point when I knew that I'd never actually find something I wanted or buy it if I did, I got into the habit of looking. I got into the habit of puzzling over lives caught in the snapshot of a realtor's open house.

—*Lucy Honig*

On a warm spring morning several years ago, I went to the beach to write. I was "interrupted" by a small, elderly woman in a white sweater, who sat next to me and told me stories for an hour, about herself and her family. Although I did not commit a single word to paper that day, I did some of my best work nonetheless: I listened. "Say to the Waves" grew out of this experience, and others like it. I am learning that writing fiction is as much—or more—about input than output. And that's a great excuse to go back to the beach.

—*Paul Michel*

I took this photograph recently on the road where "Among the Living Amidst the Trees" begins. It had been almost ten years since I'd last driven this stretch of highway, and I was both surprised and pleased to see that Route 96 is much larger, much busier, than I had remembered. The inaccuracy of my memory made me feel less trepidation about fictionalizing the town of Jasper, including its roads and establishments and citizens. So, for the lawyers, let me say this: This story is entirely a work of fiction, and while Jasper is a real Texas pineywoods town and, tragically, a town where James Byrd Jr. really was dragged to death by real bigots on a road that's really named Huff Creek Road, this story and everything in it are the products of my imagination. What I wanted, in writing this story, was to find empathy with the people of a town that had been wholly smeared in reputation by the acts of a few. What I wanted, and what I always want when I sit down to write a story, was to teach myself something—in this case, something about the buoyancy of compassion.

—Bruce Machart

I'm known among my friends for having a pretty sharp memory, so it seems strange to me that I can barely remember writing "Train Wreck with Cattle." I put the story aside when I became too deeply involved in the novel I was writing to work on anything else. A couple of years later, when I was finished with the novel and trying to complete a collection of stories, I remembered "Train Wreck with Cattle" and hunted down the hard copy. To my surprise, I discovered the story was all but finished already. I spent a day or two rewriting the last couple of paragraphs and polishing the sentences so each one rang with the sound of my narrator's somewhat desperate voice. Then there it was, a whole story, nearly abandoned by its creator, patiently awaiting its chance to strike out into the world.

I consider "Train Wreck with Cattle" a strange gift of a story, years in the making, although I didn't spend years working on it. Or I don't think I did. Like I've said, I've forgotten... although as I write this note, other memories of writing this story are starting to surface. Are these real memories, or ones my mind is unconsciously inventing because I've been trying so hard to remember?

I think it's best if I not even go there.

—*Robert Schirmer*

Sometimes a story will suggest itself to me via a first line. And sometimes the story goes no further than that—just a line, just an unrealized ache, just a flicker that eventually fades and winds up exiled somewhere in my computer's hard drive. Fortunately with "Rough" more came after the first line. The idea (I think) was to create a story that was relatively short and compact yet presented a marriage in a sweeping, almost novelistic manner (I think, I hope), cutting back and forth between the time when a couple first meets and begins to fall in love, and then to various points in their ongoing lives—from their wedding and the birth of their children to middle age and death. And plus I'd been wanting to include that bit about *The French Lieutenant's Woman* in a story for years. That part about the film class was pinched from my collegiate days. (The interpretation came from a wonderful teacher I had as an undergraduate, Professor Nelson.) Everything else I made up.

—*Andrew Roe*

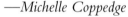

Goodbye June —
Once and for all.
Goodbye June —
I'll never see you again.

Time goes so fast!
Before you realize it
You're twelve, looking back,
wishing to still be eleven

These are the first lines of my earliest "serious" poem, written
in June 1989. I love the earnest, melodramatic girl I was. I remember sitting with my notebook on the screened porch at my grandparents' house that hot night, feeling acutely aware of how fleeting
everything was, how I could hold onto nothing. I tried to make the
night last by writing it down, even if it was changed before the pen
stopped moving. That's what I want to do when I write: capture a
moment, a feeling, somehow so I won't forget.

Below is a family shot taken the year before I wrote "Goodbye
June." It's Lisa's sixth birthday. Adrienne and Kevin look on cutely,
and I'm the big sister in the back wondering what silly Michael's
doing. Youngest brother John is not yet born. My family are all crazy,
and I love them. My amazing mother definitely "had her hands full,"
as people were always saying to her. Now she and Dad only have two
left at home.

—*Michelle Coppedge*

I remember sitting alone in a sleeper bus at a dingy station in Guang-zhou, waiting for the bus to depart for Xian. It was a sweltering day in July, the air was thick with exhaust, and I'd been waiting for almost three hours. The buses ran on no set schedule. I could speak only four words of Chinese and had no way of finding out when the bus would be leaving. So I just sat there with the torn ticket going soft and damp in my hands, and waited. This young Chinese girl was sitting on a bench beside my bus, elbows to knees, head in her hands, staring straight ahead. She looked as bored and hot and worn out as I was; I wished I could speak the language so that I could learn her story.

It got me to thinking about how we end up where we are—on this particular spot on this particular planet at this particular moment—instead of somewhere else. I thought about how random are the events that lead us to one outcome as opposed to another. It's an idea that has unsettled me my entire life, but it crystallized there, at that hot, hazy bus station in China.

Maybe "The Hero of Queens Boulevard" had its seed in that moment. And then there was the afternoon in Manhattan that my husband came home from work and told me how he'd rescued a woman from an overturned Jeep Cherokee on Queens Boulevard. So often stories come from a slow-cooked idea that collides with an actual event. William Carlos Williams said "No ideas but in things." The idea for me was that of parallel universes, and the thing was my husband's rather accidental moment of heroism.

—*Michelle Richmond*

"Hot House" has been a rare story for me in a number of ways, not least of which is that all these months later I still admire it, and there are lines that still make me laugh. While many of the sentences felt inevitable, the structure of intercutting the past and the present emerged after several drafts. I have long been fascinated by the line, at times tenuous, that separates the well from the sick, how sickness manifests itself, the ways we try to help, and the ways we fail to help. "Hot House" is part of a collection exploring these themes.

—*Jenni Lapidus*

Print by Sember Weinman

A few years ago, I came across several old Little Golden Books of various science topics: Weather, Plants, Oceanography, and Birds. These books are beautiful gems, and I became especially captivated by the descriptions about bird watching. To me, it sounded very much like the writing process: observation, stillness, recording details, setting. I had been mulling over a story in which a young girl becomes aware of her mother's relationship with a neighbor. Children, like birdwatchers and writers, possess amazing intuition and skills of observation. Somehow, making this character an amateur ornithologist, spoke to me about writing and about that scary yet beautiful place between childhood and adolescence when the world starts taking on new shapes and adults become alien. Once Alice became an ornithologist, the story took on a depth and complexity that had eluded my earlier efforts.

—*Ann Hood*

For the first six years of his life, my eight-year-old son saw everything in duplicate and triplicate, depending on the distance. Often images were reversed. After two years of vision therapy, his vision has been corrected. His drawing skill still frustrates him, but when he works on the computer, he has a great time. What I love about his work is the rhythm, joy, and refusal to abandon the way he saw the world for six years of his life.

My great-grandmother had that same combination of joy and independence. Two parts of "Avó" are true. My great-grandmother really did dump her husband's belongings in the river, and, although she drove all over Central California, she only moved forward, refusing to place herself in a position where she'd have to back up.

—*Kelly Malone*

M y son and I had moved to Connecticut, far away from my mom and dad in Texas, and we were visiting the harbor for the first time. I have always loved this picture. I was pointing out a tugboat in the distance, and the wind was strong and cool, Trevor and I were starting a new adventure in life and I was going to show him the world. Now, at ten, he's the one who points out the purple sunset, the three-legged toad on the porch, and his own emerging "six-pack" abs (a visually challenging task on my part). He teaches me the discipline of writing by sitting for hours at the computer, writing his own short stories.

—*Lori Ann Stephens*

George A. Howland Sr. and Blanche Davies Howland,
a couple since they were thirteen years old. 1953.

COMING SOON

It was one of those random realizations that can stop you short from time to time: that we were getting older, that there was so much life behind us and a whole world of worries and sickness looming just ahead: heart palpitations, enlarged prostates, strokes, dark spots on lungs and liver and brain, a whole jittering rolodex of possible cancers. We had started into the woods.

from "When I Consider How My Light Is Spent" by Travis Holland

The meal and the guests were to be lassoed together into one moment, secured by the palpable bright fabric of his words. We have much to be thankful for, we have so much to be thankful for, he began to think as the alarm clock bored into his restless sleep.

from "Thanksgiving with the Scheffels" by Yelizaveta P. Renfro

After dinner, Chencha brought out the coffee and the pralines and the two women sat on the terrace listening to the soft thud of bugs against the bougainvillea.

from "The Marvelous Yellow Cage" by Charlotte Forbes

Andrew stands at the window looking out at the dark street, waiting for his friends: Susan and Ray, Elizabeth and Mark. They're late. The married are always late.

from "Sleeping Beauty" by Kevin Canty